electricity
six

Hayden Electricity One—Seven Series

Harry Mileaf, Editor-in-Chief

electricity one Producing Electricity □ Atomic Theory □ Electrical Charges □ Electron Theory □ Current □ Voltage □ Magnetism □ Electromagnetism

electricity two D-C Circuits □ Direct Current □ Resistors □ Ohm's Law □ Power □ Series Circuits □ Parallel Circuits □ Series-Parallel Circuits □ Kirchhoff's Laws □ Superposition □ Thevenin's Theorem □ Norton's Theorem

electricity three A-C Circuits □ Alternating Current □ A-C Waveforms □ Resistive Circuits □ Inductors □ Inductive Circuits □ Transformers □ Capacitors □ Capacitive Circuits

electricity four LCR Circuits □ Vectors □ RL Circuits □ RC Circuits □ LC Circuits □ Series-Parallel Circuits □ Resonant Circuits □ Filters

electricity five Test Equipment □ Meter Movements □ Ammeters □ Voltmeters □ Ohmmeters □ Wattmeters □ Multimeters □ Vacuum-Tube Voltmeters

electricity six Power Sources □ Primary Cells □ Batteries □ Photo, Thermo, Solar Cells □ D-C Generators □ A-C Generators □ Motor-Generators □ Dynamotors

electricity seven Electric Motors □ D-C Motors □ A-C Motors □ Synchronous Motors □ Induction Motors □ Reluctance Motors □ Hysteresis Motors □ Repulsion Motors □ Universal Motors □ Starters □ Controllers

electricity
six

HARRY MILEAF EDITOR-IN-CHIEF

revised second edition

HAYDEN BOOKS

A Division of Howard W. Sams & Company
4300 West 62nd Street
Indianapolis, Indiana 46268 USA

©1966 and 1976 by Hayden Books
A Division of Howard W. Sams & Co.

SECOND EDITION
NINTH PRINTING — 1989

International Standard Book Number: *0-8104-5950-7*
Library of Congress Catalog Card Number: *75-45504*

Printed in United States of America

preface

This volume is one of a series designed specifically to teach electricity. The series is logically organized to fit the learning process. Each volume covers a given area of knowledge, which in itself is complete, but also prepares the student for the ensuing volumes. Within each volume, the topics are taught in incremental steps and each topic treatment prepares the student for the next topic. Only *one* discrete topic or concept is examined on a page, and *each* page carries an illustration that graphically depicts the topic being covered. As a result of this treatment, neither the text nor the illustrations are relied on solely as a teaching medium for any given topic. Both are given for *every* topic, so that the illustrations not only complement but reinforce the text. In addition, to further aid the student in retaining what he has learned, the important points are summarized in text form on the illustration. This unique treatment allows the book to be used as a convenient review text. Color is used not for decorative purposes, but to accent important points and make the illustrations meaningful.

In keeping with good teaching practice, all technical terms are defined at their point of introduction so that the student can proceed with confidence. And, to facilitate matters for both the student and the teacher, key words for each topic are made conspicuous by the use of italics. Major points covered in prior topics are often reiterated in later topics for purposes of retention. This allows not only the smooth transition from topic to topic, but the reinforcement of prior knowledge just before the declining point of one's memory curve. At the end of each group of topics comprising a lesson, a summary of the facts is given, together with an appropriate set of review questions, so that the student himself can determine how well he is learning as he proceeds through the book.

Much of the credit for the development of this series belongs to various members of the excellent team of authors, editors, and technical consultants assembled by the publisher. Special acknowledgment of the contributions of the following individuals is most appropriate: Frank T. Egan, Jack Greenfield, and Warren W. Yates, principal contributors; Peter J. Zurita, Steven Barbash, Solomon Flam, and A. Victor Schwarz, of the publisher's staff; Paul J. Barotta, Director of the Union Technical Institute; Albert J. Marcarelli, Technical Director of the Connecticut School of Electronics; Howard Bierman, Editor of *Electronic Design;* E. E. Grazda, Editorial Director of *Electronic Design;* and Irving Lopatin, Editorial Director of the Hayden Book Companies.

HARRY MILEAF
Editor-in-Chief

contents

CONTENTS

power sources

In previous volumes of this series, you studied what electricity is, how it is put to practical use in electrical circuits, and how it is measured. You will now learn about devices that produce electricity. These devices are called *power sources*.

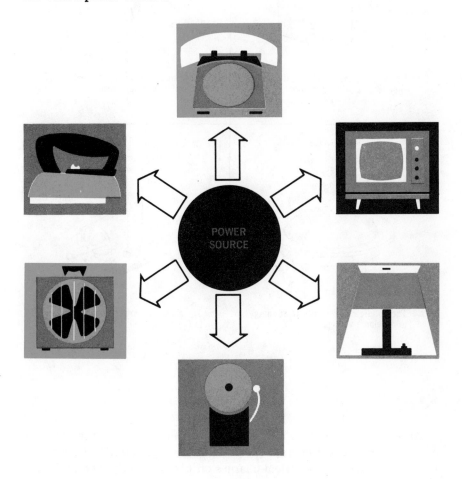

The power source supplies the electricity needed to operate electrical equipment

When a load is connected to a power source, electric current flows from the source to the load. The power source must supply the amount of voltage and current that the load needs. Any load, such as a lamp or motor, can only work as well as the power source will permit.

BATTERY

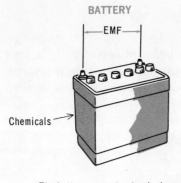

Chemicals

The battery converts chemical energy
to build up a difference of potential

THERMOCOUPLE

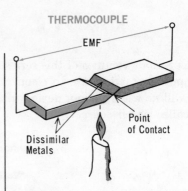

Point
of Contact

Dissimilar
Metals

The thermocouple converts heat energy
to develop an electromotive force

PHOTOVOLTAIC CELL

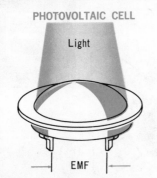

Light

EMF

The voltaic cell converts light energy
to develop a voltage

GENERATOR

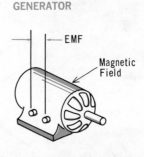

EMF

Magnetic
Field

The generator converts magnetic energy
to induce an emf

types

Power sources produce electricity by converting some other form of energy into electrical energy. Power sources supply electrical energy by building up opposite electrical charges on two *terminals*. The *difference of potential*, or *electromotive force* (emf), between these terminals moves the electric current through the load that is connected across the source. The most common power sources you will encounter are the *battery, thermocouple, photovoltaic cell,* and *generator.* They all supply an electric voltage and current, but each converts different forms of energy. The *battery* converts *chemical energy*, the *thermocouple* converts *heat energy*, the *photovoltaic cell* converts *light energy*, and the *generator* converts *magnetic energy*.

the battery

The battery is one of the most important power sources in use today because its energy is *self-contained*. This is one advantage that none of the other power sources have. All the power sources must first be supplied with outside energy, such as heat, light, or mechanical energy, before they can produce electricity. However, the electrical energy of the battery is produced by the chemical energy contained within the battery.

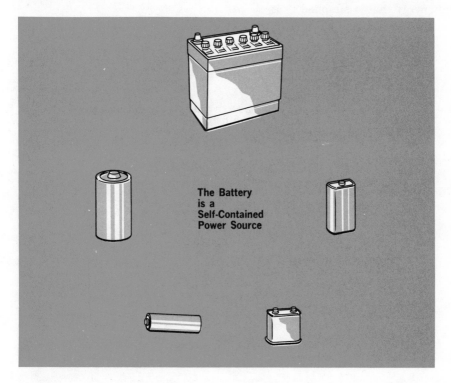

**The Battery
is a
Self-Contained
Power Source**

The battery is used mostly wherever a *portable* power source is required, such as in flashights and lanterns, in the automobile electrical system, in photography to ignite flash bulbs and photoflash lamps, and in portable radios, measuring instruments, and hearing aids to supply the electronic circuits; they are also used in trains, planes, and ships, toys, special clocks and watches, etc. In fact, the battery is the most versatile power source in use today. The battery is also used as a calibrated source of voltage in a voltage *standard*. Typical of this is the standard cell used by the National Bureau of Standards to establish other units of electricity, such as the ohm and the ampere.

types of batteries

Basically, batteries are classified as *primary* or *secondary* according to the manner in which their chemical energy is converted into electrical energy. The *primary battery* converts chemical energy to electrical energy *directly*, using the chemical materials within the cell to start the action. The *secondary battery* must first be *charged* with electrical energy before it can convert chemical energy to electrical energy. The secondary battery is frequently called a *storage battery*, since it stores the energy that is supplied to it.

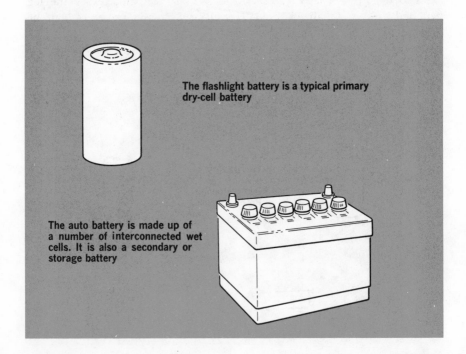

The flashlight battery is a typical primary dry-cell battery

The auto battery is made up of a number of interconnected wet cells. It is also a secondary or storage battery

Batteries are also classified as wet cells or dry cells. The *wet* cell battery uses *liquid* chemicals, while the so-called *dry* cell contains a chemical paste. The *cell* is the basic unit of a battery. A *battery* often consists of a number of cells connected to supply a voltage or current greater than that of a single cell. However, the terms cell and battery are now frequently used interchangeably.

The primary battery is used mostly where a limited current is required. The primary batteries you will probably see most commonly are the dry cells. The secondary battery is generally used where a heavy current is required; secondary batteries are usually wet cells.

early history

Although the discovery of electricity dates back about 2500 years to the ancient Greeks, very little progress in the science of electricity was made until the basic cell was discovered in the late eighteenth century. Up to that time, there was no *convenient* source of electrical energy.

The action of the basic cell was first noticed by Luigi Galvani in 1791, while he was preparing an experiment in anatomy. For the experiment, Galvani had removed dissected frog legs from a salt solution and suspended them by means of a copper wire. He noticed that each time he touched one of the legs with an iron scalpel, the muscles of the leg twitched. Galvani realized that electricity was being produced, but he thought it came from the leg muscles.

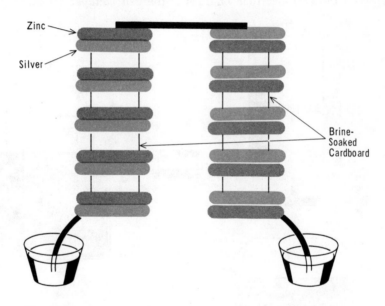

The voltaic pile uses an alternating stack of silver and zinc discs separated by discs of cardboard soaked with a salt solution. This was the first battery

In 1800, Alessandro Volta repeated the experiment, and found that the muscles of the frog did not produce the electricity. Instead, he discovered that the electricity was the result of a chemical action between the copper wire, iron scalpel, and salt solution. Using this knowledge, he built the first practical electric battery, which is known as the *voltaic pile*.

the basic primary wet cell

After Alessandro Volta made his first battery, he continued to experiment with metals and chemicals. He found that by putting two *different metals* in certain chemical solutions, electricity could still be produced. This is the basic primary wet cell. In his honor, it is usually called the *voltaic cell;* however, it is also sometimes referred to as the *galvanic cell,* in honor of Galvani.

The metals in a cell are called the *electrodes,* and the chemical solution is called the *electrolyte.* The electrolyte reacts oppositely with the two different electrodes. It causes one electrode to lose electrons and develop a *positive charge;* and it causes the other electrode to build up a surplus of electrons and develop a *negative charge.* The difference in potential between the two electrode charges is the cell *voltage.*

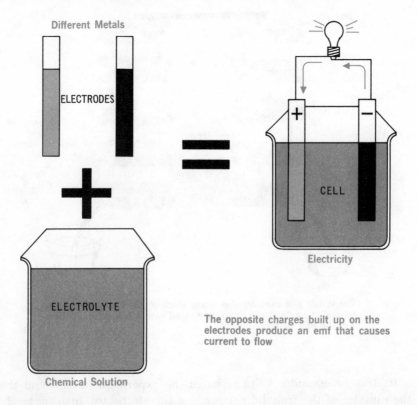

Different Metals

ELECTRODES

ELECTROLYTE

Chemical Solution

CELL

Electricity

The opposite charges built up on the electrodes produce an emf that causes current to flow

In the basic battery you will study on the following pages, copper and zinc will be used for the electrodes, and sulfuric acid mixed with water will be the electrolyte. Actually, as you will learn later, a number of different metals and chemicals can be used.

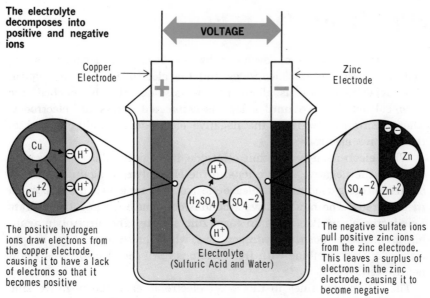

The electrolyte decomposes into positive and negative ions

VOLTAGE

Copper Electrode

Zinc Electrode

The positive hydrogen ions draw electrons from the copper electrode, causing it to have a lack of electrons so that it becomes positive

Electrolyte (Sulfuric Acid and Water)

The negative sulfate ions pull positive zinc ions from the zinc electrode. This leaves a surplus of electrons in the zinc electrode, causing it to become negative

A voltage is developed between the two charged electrodes

developing a voltage

Sulfuric acid mixed with water breaks down into hydrogen ions and sulfate ions. There are two *positive hydrogen ions* produced for each *negative sulfate ion,* but each hydrogen ion has one positive charge ($H+$), while each sulfate ion has two negative charges (SO_4^{-2}). Therefore, the entire solution is *neutral.* When the zinc electrode is placed in the solution, the sulfate ions attack the zinc, causing its atoms to give off electrons. The negative sulfate ions attract positive zinc ions (Zn^{+2}) from the electrode, but the electrons released by the zinc atoms remain. So, the *zinc electrode* builds up a *surplus of electrons* and a *negative charge.*

When it develops a sufficient negative charge, the zinc electrode repels the sulfate ions to prevent further activity. The zinc ions then combine with sulfate ions to form neutral zinc sulfate molecules. The electrolyte then has more positive charges than negative charges. As a result, when the copper is placed in the electrolyte, the positive hydrogen ions attract free electrons from the copper. These electrons combine with the hydrogen atoms to neutralize them. This continues until enough hydrogen ions are neutralized to make the electrolyte neutral again. Because of this, the copper electrode develops a *lack of electrons* and a *positive charge.* The *difference in potential* between the positive electrode and the negative electrode produces a *voltage* across the electrodes.

supplying current

The value of voltage developed by the basic cell depends on the materials used for the electrodes and the electrolyte. For the typical zinc-copper cells, this is about 1.08 volts. Once this is reached, the chemical action stops until a load is connected across the electrodes. Then electrons flow from the negative electrode through the load to the positive electrode.

When electrons leave the zinc electrode, its negative charge is reduced, allowing the negative sulfate ions in the electrolyte to again attack the electrode. More zinc atoms release electrons to replenish the supply in the electrode. The new positive zinc ions combine with negative sulfate ions in the electrolyte to again form zinc sulfate. The electrolyte again has an excess of positive hydrogen ions, which are drawn to the copper electrode; they combine with free electrons until the electrolyte is again neutralized.

The action continues in this way: electrons leave the negative zinc electrode and flow through the load to the positive copper electrode; the electrons leaving the zinc are replaced by those that are left behind by the zinc sulfate; and the electrons that enter the copper replace those that leave to neutralize the hydrogen ions. In this manner, the charge on each electrode is kept almost constant, and the terminal voltage remains steady as the cell delivers current.

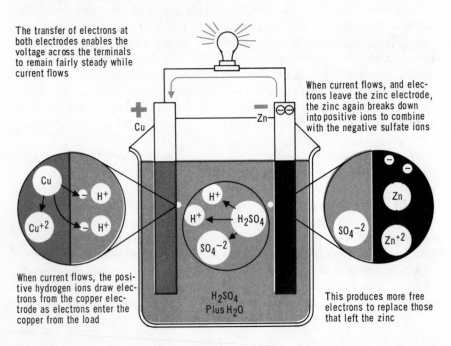

The transfer of electrons at both electrodes enables the voltage across the terminals to remain fairly steady while current flows

When current flows, and electrons leave the zinc electrode, the zinc again breaks down into positive ions to combine with the negative sulfate ions

When current flows, the positive hydrogen ions draw electrons from the copper electrode as electrons enter the copper from the load

This produces more free electrons to replace those that left the zinc

local action

The chemical action in the basic wet primary cell should stop when the cell is not delivering current. This is not always the case, however, because there are some impurities in the electrode material, such as iron (Fe) and carbon (C). These impurities *react* with the zinc and the electrolyte to form many *small cells* that produce local electrical currents about the zinc electrode. This *local action* occurs in the cell whether or not the cell is delivering current. As a result, the electrolyte and electrodes are used unnecessarily, and the battery will not last as long as it should.

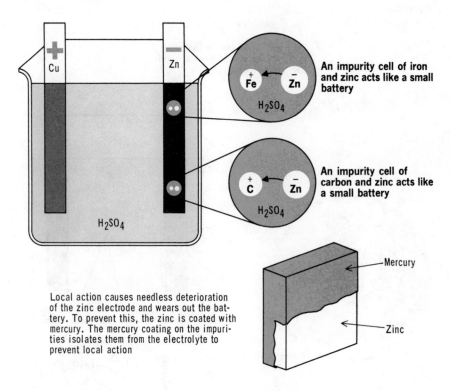

An impurity cell of iron and zinc acts like a small battery

An impurity cell of carbon and zinc acts like a small battery

Local action causes needless deterioration of the zinc electrode and wears out the battery. To prevent this, the zinc is coated with mercury. The mercury coating on the impurities isolates them from the electrolyte to prevent local action

To reduce the amount of local action that exists, *mercury* is coated on the surface of the zinc electrode. This process is called *amalgamation*. The zinc dissolves in the mercury but is still free to combine with the electrolyte. The impurities, however, do not dissolve in the mercury; instead, they are coated with it, and so are isolated from the electrolyte. Therefore, they cannot combine with the electrolyte to produce local action.

polarization

When the positive hydrogen ions draw electrons from the copper electrodes, neutral hydrogen gas bubbles are formed. Some of these bubbles cling to the copper electrode and produce a layer of nonconducting gas around it. This gas interferes with the action of the cell in two ways. First, the gas bubbles *reduce the effective area* of the copper electrode, so that fewer hydrogen ions can reach it. Second, the positive hydrogen ions tend to collect around these bubbles. This causes a local positive charge to be built up in the electrolyte, which repels the positive hydrogen ions away from the copper electrode. This effect is known as *polarization*.

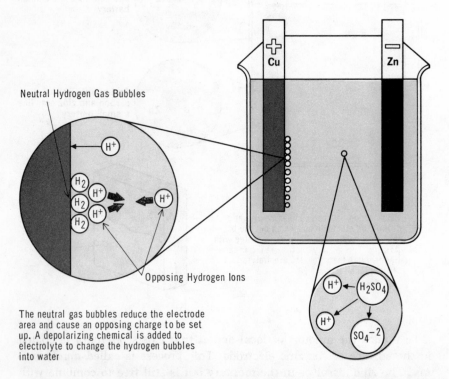

Polarization is due to the neutral gas bubbles that collect around the positive electrode

Neutral Hydrogen Gas Bubbles

Opposing Hydrogen Ions

The neutral gas bubbles reduce the electrode area and cause an opposing charge to be set up. A depolarizing chemical is added to electrolyte to change the hydrogen bubbles into water

To remove the neutral hydrogen gas bubbles, a depolarizer is added to the electrolyte. Usually a chemical such as *manganese dioxide* is used. This reacts with the hydrogen gas bubbles to form water. The water then merely mixes with the electrolyte, and polarization is prevented.

the electrolyte

For the basic zinc-copper cell you have studied until now, the electrolyte used was sulfuric acid mixed with water. Actually, many different chemicals can be used. The important functions that the chemicals must perform are

1. Break down into positive and negative ions when they are mixed with water.
2. React chemically with at least one of the electrodes.

Since different chemicals react more or less with different metals, the electrolyte used will determine the actual charges produced on the electrodes, and will determine the amount of voltage and current the battery can supply. Some other electrolytes are ammonium chloride (NH_4Cl), which breaks into positive ammonium ions (NH_4^+) and negative chloride ions (Cl^-); and copper sulfate, which breaks down into positive copper ions (Cu^{+2}) and negative sulfate ions (SO_4^{-2}).

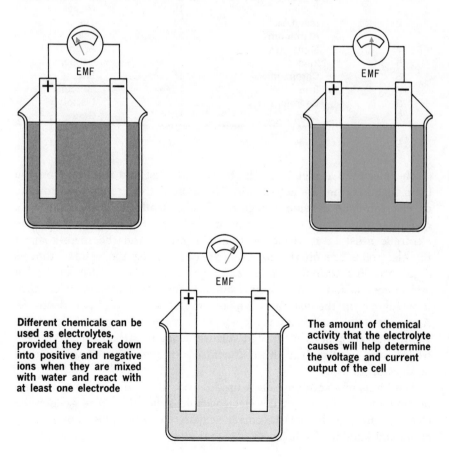

Different chemicals can be used as electrolytes, provided they break down into positive and negative ions when they are mixed with water and react with at least one electrode

The amount of chemical activity that the electrolyte causes will help determine the voltage and current output of the cell

the electrodes

The metals used for the electrodes in the basic cell are chosen so that when they react with the electrolyte, one will give up electrons to develop a *positive* charge, while the other will take on electrons to develop a *negative* charge. The tendency of a metal to give up or take on electrons depends on how *active* the metal is chemically. A special list of metals has been made up to show how active one metal is compared to others. This list is known as the *electromotive* or *galvanic series* of metals, and a partial list is shown.

PARTIAL LISTING OF ELECTROMOTIVE SERIES

Order of Activity	Metal	Order of Activity	Metal
1	Sodium	10	Nickel
2	Magnesium	11	Tin
3	Aluminum	12	Lead
4	Manganese	13	Antimony
5	Zinc	14	Copper
6	Chromium	15	Silver
7	Iron	16	Mercury
8	Cadmium	17	Platinum
9	Cobalt	18	Gold

The most active metals are highest on the list and the lower on the list a metal is, the less active it is. The more active metals tend to take on electrons and develop a negative charge, while the less active ones give up electrons and produce a positive charge. For a cell to work, one electrode must be more active than the other. And the farther apart the electrodes are on the list, the greater will be the voltage that is developed. For example, for the zinc-copper cell, zinc is fifth on the list and copper is fourteenth. Zinc would be the negative electrode, since it is higher on the list; and copper would be the positive electrode. Approximately 1.08 volts is developed between these two electrodes when they are placed in diluted sulfuric acid. If carbon and zinc electrodes were used with a chromic acid electrolyte, about 2 volts would be developed.

The kinds of electrode metals used do not affect the current capacity of the battery. The size of the electrodes does, however. The greater the electrode size, the higher the current capacity will be. This is more fully explained later in the book.

limitations

The primary wet cell has two basic disadvantages. The first is that its operation relies on the necessity for the electrolyte to attack the negative electrode to produce the chemical action. As a result, as the battery is used, the negative electrode slowly disintegrates. And, when much of it is gone, it cannot supply the amount of current needed. In addition, the electrolyte, too, undergoes a chemical change as it reacts with both electrodes; after a while, the chemical nature of the electrolyte changes to such a degree that it loses much of its electrolytic properties and cannot build up enough of a charge on each electrode. However, the primary wet cell can be restored by replacing the negative electrode and the electrolyte. But this brings us to the second disadvantage.

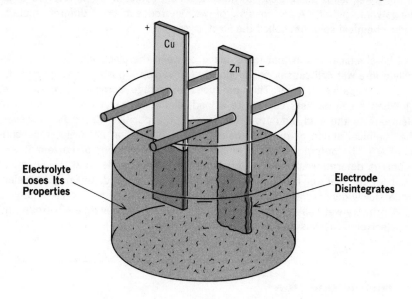

The primary wet cell works in such a way that the negative electrode slowly disintegrates and the electrolyte loses its properties. To make it easy to repair, it is inconvenient to use it commercially

If the wet cell is made so that it is easy to repair, it cannot be convenient, since it uses a liquid electrolyte. If it were made rugged and spillproof so that it would be portable, it would be difficult to repair, and expensive to replace. As a result, most primary wet cells in use today are simply constructed for laboratory use.

For convenient, inexpensive, commercial use, the primary dry battery was developed.

summary

☐ Power sources are devices that produce electricity by converting some other forms of energy into electrical energy. ☐ A battery is a power source that converts chemical energy into electrical energy. ☐ The energy of a battery is self-contained, so batteries are ideally suited for applications requiring a portable source of power. ☐ A primary battery converts chemical energy directly into electrical energy. ☐ A secondary battery first has to be charged with electrical energy before it can produce an electrical output. Secondary batteries are often called storage batteries.

☐ The cell is the basic unit of a battery. ☐ Wet cells use liquid chemicals; while dry cells contain a chemical paste. ☐ Primary batteries are usually of the dry-cell type, and secondary batteries of the wet-cell type. ☐ The basic primary wet cell is usually called the voltaic cell; sometimes it is referred to as the galvanic cell. ☐ A cell consists of two electrodes made of different metals, and a chemical solution, called the electrolyte.

☐ The chemical action that takes place between the electrodes and the electrolyte in a wet cell causes one electrode to develop a positive charge and the other a negative charge. This produces a voltage across the electrodes. ☐ When a cell delivers current to a load, electrons travel from the negative electrode to the load, and from the load to the positive electrode. However, the chemical action of the cell maintains the charge on each electrode constant. ☐ The output voltage of a battery and the amount of current it can supply is determined by the metals used for the electrodes and the chemical used for the electrolyte. ☐ As a primary wet cell is used, the negative electrode slowly disintegrates and the chemical nature of the electrolyte changes. ☐ A primary wet cell can be restored by replacing the negative electrode and the electrolyte. This is usually impractical, though.

review questions

1. What is the difference between a *primary* battery and a *secondary* battery?
2. What is a *wet cell?* A *dry cell?*
3. Name the basic parts of a battery.
4. Briefly describe how a wet cell develops a voltage.
5. What is meant by *local action?*
6. What is a *depolarizer?*
7. What determines the voltage developed by a basic cell?
8. The electrolyte in a cell must perform what two functions?
9. What is the *electromotive series of metals?*
10. What are the disadvantages of the primary wet cell?

the basic primary dry cell

The so-called dry cell actually uses an *electrolytic paste*. The paste is very thick and does not have a tendency to spill or leak. As a result, the dry battery can be made cheaply and light in weight, and are the batteries that are used extensively by the public and industry.

The dry cell works in a manner that is similar to the wet cell. The electrolytic paste reacts with the electrodes to produce a negative charge on one electrode and a positive charge on the other. The difference in potential between the two electrodes is the output voltage.

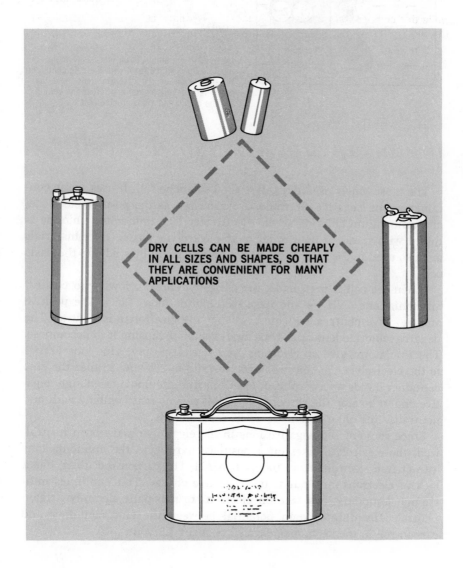

DRY CELLS CAN BE MADE CHEAPLY IN ALL SIZES AND SHAPES, SO THAT THEY ARE CONVENIENT FOR MANY APPLICATIONS

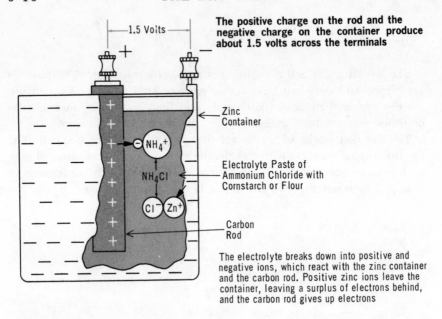

The positive charge on the rod and the negative charge on the container produce about 1.5 volts across the terminals

1.5 Volts

Zinc Container

Electrolyte Paste of Ammonium Chloride with Cornstarch or Flour

Carbon Rod

The electrolyte breaks down into positive and negative ions, which react with the zinc container and the carbon rod. Positive zinc ions leave the container, leaving a surplus of electrons behind, and the carbon rod gives up electrons

the basic zinc-carbon dry cell

The most widely used dry cell is the Leclanche cell. It uses a zinc container as the negative electrode, a carbon rod as the positive electrode, and ammonium chloride as the electrolyte. The ammonium chloride is mixed with starch or flour to make an electrolytic paste. Other materials are also used in the Leclanche cell, but let us begin by studying the basic cell.

When the cell is first made, the electrolyte breaks down into positive ammonia ions (NH_4^+) and negative chloride ions (Cl^-). The positive and negative charges are equal, so that the electrolyte is neutral. The negative chloride ions attack the zinc container causing it to decompose. The zinc atoms give up electrons, and release positive zinc ions (Zn^+) to the electrolyte. The electrons stay behind in the zinc so that the zinc container builds up a surplus of electrons and accumulates enough negative charge to stop the activity. The positive zinc ions combine with and neutralize the chloride ions to form zinc chloride.

Since some of the negative ions in the electrolyte have been neutralized, the electrolyte takes on a positive charge and the ammonia ions attract free electrons from the carbon rod. The carbon rod, then, has a lack of electrons, and builds up a positive charge. This continues until enough ammonia ions take on electrons to make the electrolyte again neutral. The difference in potential between the zinc container and carbon rod in the Leclanche dry cell is about 1.5 volts.

polarization and local action

Dry cells suffer from the effects of polarization and local action in the same way as wet cells, and the conditions are corrected for in a similar manner. The zinc container in a dry cell is usually amalgamated to reduce local action.

For polarization, the Leclanche dry cell uses a mixture of carbon powder, manganese dioxide, and zinc chloride. The carbon powder acts as a pasty binder when mixed with the chemicals.

The dry cell also develops polarization and local action

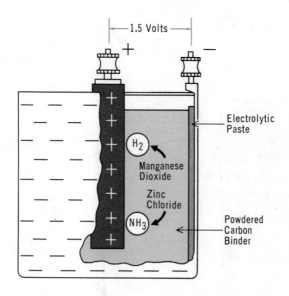

The zinc container is usually amalgamated to keep local action down. And the polarization, due to hydrogen gas (H_2) and ammonia gas (NH_3), is reduced when manganese dioxide and zinc chloride are used. These chemicals are mixed with a powdered carbon binder

When the ammonia ions (NH_4^+) react with the carbon rod, they change into ammonia and hydrogen gas bubbles. The manganese dioxide combines with the hydrogen gas to form water, and the zinc chloride combines with the ammonia gas to form ammonium chloride. This removes the gas bubbles from around the carbon rod, and the resultant chemicals mix with the powdered carbon.

construction of the leclanche dry cell

As you have seen, the dry cell has a considerably different construction than the wet cell. A typical flashlight battery is shown. The cap on the carbon rod is the positive terminal, and the bottom of the zinc container is the negative terminal. Seals are used to make the battery relatively leakproof, and a paper-like cover is generally glued around the zinc container to act as an insulator and to contain information about the battery.

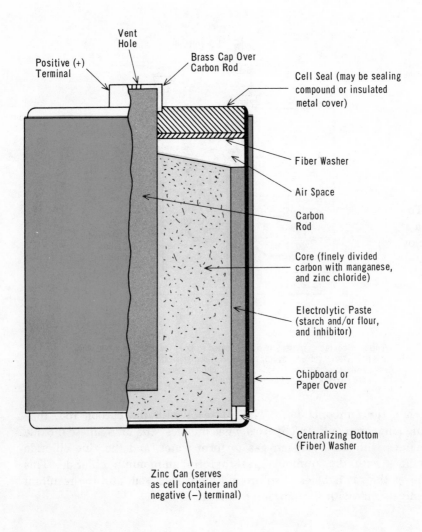

Vent Hole

Positive (+) Terminal

Brass Cap Over Carbon Rod

Cell Seal (may be sealing compound or insulated metal cover)

Fiber Washer

Air Space

Carbon Rod

Core (finely divided carbon with manganese, and zinc chloride)

Electrolytic Paste (starch and/or flour, and inhibitor)

Chipboard or Paper Cover

Centralizing Bottom (Fiber) Washer

Zinc Can (serves as cell container and negative (−) terminal)

leakproof dry cells

Although the ordinary dry cell uses seals to make it leakproof, it will remain sealed only as long as the zinc container remains intact. However, as you remember, the battery works because the electrolyte attacks the zinc container, and as the battery delivers current, the container is slowly eaten away as it forms zinc chloride with the electrolyte. When the zinc container wears out and develops holes, the battery is no longer leakproof. Moisture can seep in and cause the battery to swell up. And the zinc chloride that forms when the electrolyte reacts with the zinc container can leak out. The white substance that you see on worn out batteries is zinc chloride.

When the zinc container wears out, the ordinary battery is no longer leakproof

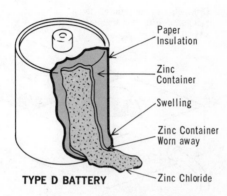

Paper Insulation

Zinc Container

Swelling

Zinc Container Worn away

Zinc Chloride

TYPE D BATTERY

To prevent this swelling and leaking, the better batteries are encased in a *steel jacket*. The rest of the battery is made slightly smaller, so that the overall battery size does not change. A paper tube is placed between the steel jacket and zinc container for insulation purposes.

TYPE D BATTERY

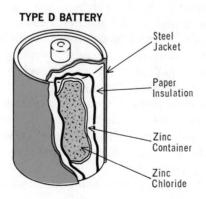

Steel Jacket

Paper Insulation

Zinc Container

Zinc Chloride

When the zinc container deteriorates to the point where holes are developed, the steel jacket prevents moisture from seeping in and chemicals from seeping out. The steel-jacketed batteries are leakproof

rejuvenation

Like the wet cell, the basic primary dry cell deteriorates while it is being used. Zinc atoms from the negative electrode are carried into the electrolyte while the cell is being used, and when much of the electrode is eaten away, the cell becomes useless. Unlike the electrodes in a wet cell, the electrodes in a dry cell cannot be replaced. If there is extensive damage to the electrode, the cell must be replaced. But if the damage is not extensive, the operating life of the dry cell can be extended by a process known as rejuvenation.

Dry cells can sometimes be rejuvenated to extend their useful life

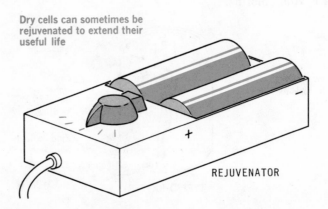

REJUVENATOR

The electrochemical process that removed particles of zinc and had them combine with the chloride atoms in the electrolyte to form zinc chloride can be reversed. This will cause the zinc chloride molecules to split, and the zinc atoms will be carried back to the negative electrode. Essentially, with a properly applied voltage and current, electroplating occurs to repair the negative electrode. But this can be done only as long as the electrode is not too disintegrated, so that too much electroplating is required. Extensive electroplating cannot be controlled, and the zinc buildup could accumulate in localized areas to cause extended sharp growths that could cause shorts. Essentially, then, the rejuvenation process must be used *before* extensive wear shows, and should be repeated regularly while the battery is in fair condition to get the most extended life. After a while, the rejuvenation process will cause the zinc build up that results in a short. Often, these dry cell rejuvenators are called chargers, but they do not really charge the battery. This is explained for the secondary, or storage, cell.

Rejuvenation of a dry cell is brought about by using a reverse voltage to apply a reverse current through the cell.

dry cell standards

It is possible to design and package the ordinary dry cell, or combinations of cells, in an infinite number of ways, to give any combination of characteristics. To prevent the confusion that might result from any lack of control, the United States of America Standards Institute issues the specifications for standard battery types and sizes, so that the dry cell batteries of different manufacturers can be interchangeable.

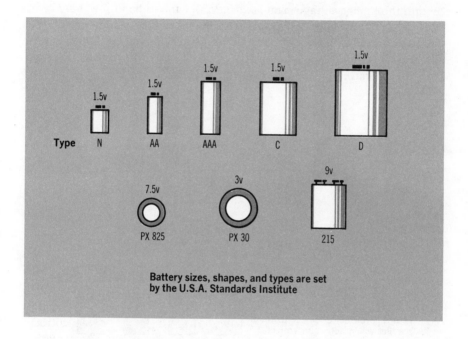

Battery sizes, shapes, and types are set
by the U.S.A. Standards Institute

There are innumerable types, and only the more popular commercial dry cells will be covered here. The Type N, AA, and AAA dry cells are typical of the batteries used in penlights, cameras, portable radios, recorders, etc. The Type C and D batteries are popular for flashlights and electrical toys, but are also used in some of the larger radios and recorders.

The Type PX 30 and PX 825 are button cells designed primarily for use in cameras. The Type 215 battery is typical of the higher voltage batteries used in portable radios, etc.

The size and shape of the battery does not always denote its voltage. For example, the N, AA, AAA, C, and D batteries are all 1.5-volt cells. Their size does, however, give them different current and life ratings, as you will soon learn.

multiple-cell batteries

You learned earlier that although the terms *cell* and *battery* are now used interchangeably, at one time, the term battery was used only to mean a combination of cells. In most applications, the voltage and current that can be supplied by a single cell is not enough, so many batteries have to use *combinations of cells*. When a *higher voltage* is needed, cells are connected in *series*, so that their emf's add. The cells can be connected within the battery, or separate batteries can be combined to obtain the higher voltage. The *polarities* all have to be in the *same direction*. If they are not, the voltages will subtract. The same current goes through all the cells in a series setup, and so this type does not increase the current rating. As a matter of fact, the overall current delivered will be the rating of the weakest cell.

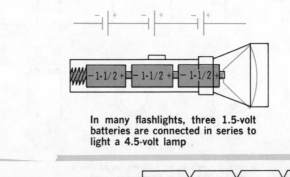

In many flashlights, three 1.5-volt batteries are connected in series to light a 4.5-volt lamp

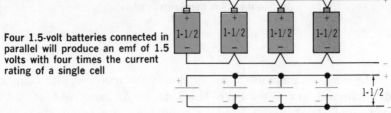

Four 1.5-volt batteries connected in parallel will produce an emf of 1.5 volts with four times the current rating of a single cell

To *increase* the *current rating,* cells must be connected in *parallel.* Then each cell will supply its own current, and the sum of all the cells will be the total current rating. Again, all of the cells should be connected with the same polarity. If not, the cells will supply current to each other and short circuit the combination. All of the cells should have the same voltage rating, otherwise the higher voltage cell will supply current to the lower voltage cell.

HOWARD W. SAMS & COMPANY

Bookmark

DEAR VALUED CUSTOMER:

Howard W. Sams & Company is dedicated to bringing you timely and authoritative books for your personal and professional library. Our goal is to provide you with excellent technical books written by the most qualified authors. You can assist us in this endeavor by checking the box next to your particular areas of interest.

We appreciate your comments and will use the information to provide you with a more comprehensive selection of titles.

Thank you,

Vice President, Book Publishing
Howard W. Sams & Company

COMPUTER TITLES:

Hardware
- ☐ Apple 140   ☐ Macintosh I01
- ☐ Commodore 110
- ☐ IBM & Compatibles 114

Business Applications
- ☐ Word Processing J01
- ☐ Data Base J04
- ☐ Spreadsheets J02

Operating Systems
- ☐ MS-DOS K05   ☐ OS/2 K10
- ☐ CP/M K01   ☐ UNIX K03

Programming Languages
- ☐ C L03   ☐ Pascal L05
- ☐ Prolog L12   ☐ Assembly L01
- ☐ BASIC L02   ☐ HyperTalk L14

Troubleshooting & Repair
- ☐ Computers S05
- ☐ Peripherals S10

Other
- ☐ Communications/Networking M03
- ☐ AI/Expert Systems T18

ELECTRONICS TITLES:

- ☐ Amateur Radio T01
- ☐ Audio T03
- ☐ Basic Electronics T20
- ☐ Basic Electricity T21
- ☐ Electronics Design T12
- ☐ Electronics Projects T04
- ☐ Satellites T09

- ☐ Instrumentation T05
- ☐ Digital Electronics T11

Troubleshooting & Repair
- ☐ Audio S11   ☐ Television S04
- ☐ VCR S01   ☐ Compact Disc S02
- ☐ Automotive S06
- ☐ Microwave Oven S03

Other interests or comments: _____

_____

_____

Name_____

Title _____

Company _____

Address _____

City _____

State/Zip _____

Daytime Telephone No. _____

A Division of Macmillan, Inc.
4300 West 62nd Street
Indianapolis, Indiana 46268

45950

Bookmark

BUSINESS REPLY CARD

FIRST CLASS   PERMIT NO. 1076   INDIANAPOLIS, IND.

POSTAGE WILL BE PAID BY ADDRESSEE

HOWARD W. SAMS & CO.
ATTN: Public Relations Department
P.O. BOX 7092
Indianapolis, IN 46209-9921

HOWARD W. SAMS
& COMPANY

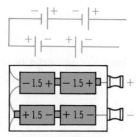

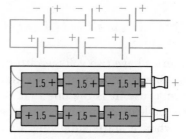

A 6-volt transistor battery contains four 1.5 volt cells in series

A 9-volt transistor radio battery contains six 1.5-volt cells in series

typical multiple-cell batteries

The previous page showed you how ordinary C or D size cells can be used together to increase voltage or current. The batteries that are available with higher voltages actually produce the higher voltage by combining a series of cells within the battery case. A 6-volt transistor battery uses four 1.5-volt cells, and a 9-volt transistor battery uses six 1.5-volt cells. A 45-volt power pack uses thirty 1.5-volt cells in series. A 90-volt pack can use two 45-volt arrangements (60 cells) or, if greater current capacity is desired, four 45-volt arrangements connected in series-parallel (120 1.5-volt cells, connected 60 to each bank). Batteries are available with the following voltages: 1,5, 3, 4.5, 6, 7.5, 9, 12, 15, 22.5, 30, 45, 67.5, 90, and so on up to 500 volts. Those from 30 to 500 volts are mostly for industrial and military use, and are hard to get commercially.

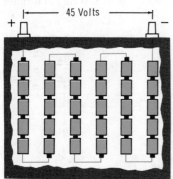

A 45-volt battery uses thirty 1.5-volt cells connected in series

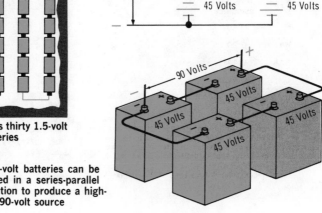

Four 45-volt batteries can be connected in a series-parallel combination to produce a high-current 90-volt source

internal resistance

Batteries have two voltage ratings: a no-load rating and a normal load rating. Since the normal load rating is the voltage that actually occurs in normal use, it is the one that is used.

The no-load rating is higher because the battery voltage actually drops when it starts supplying a current. This is because a battery has internal resistance, which results from the opposition that the electrodes and the electrolyte give to the flow of current. When the current flows through this internal resistance, a portion of the battery voltage is dropped and less is available at the output terminals. As the battery wears out, the electrodes and electrolytes in the cell deteriorate and become poorer conductors. The internal resistance increases, and the output voltage decreases further.

With a worn-out battery, the voltage drops to a point where the battery will not function properly. For example, if you had a 9-volt battery in which each of the six cells had a 0.5 ohm internal resistance, the total resistance would be 3 ohms. If the circuit had 10 ma flowing in it, the battery would drop 30 millivolts, having little effect on the 9-volt output. But if each cell deteriorated to 5 ohms, the total would become 30 ohms, and 10 ma would cause 0.9-volt to drop internally. The output would then weaken and go down to 8.1 volts.

The amount of internal resistance a battery has also determines how much peak or flash current it can supply in a short time. A low resistance is needed for high short peaks to keep the output voltage from dropping too far. This is why penlight or flashlight batteries should not be used for photoflash or transistors, even though they have the same type designation. Some typical internal resistances of different Leclanche cells are shown below:

Type	Internal resistance
N	0.69 Ω
AA	0.29 Ω
AAA	0.44 Ω
C	0.47 Ω
D	0.27 Ω

Every cell has an internal resistance that drops part of the cell voltage when current flows. The more worn out a battery is, the higher its internal resistance becomes. The output of the battery under load is

$$E_{\text{UNDER LOAD}} = E_{\text{NO LOAD}} - IR_{\text{INTERNAL}}$$

current rating/useful life

The amount of current that a battery can supply depends on the size of the electrodes and the internal resistance of the battery. Small dry cells are limited in how large their electrodes can be, so they generally strive for low internal resistances, particularly if they are designed for photoflash or transistor use.

Also, since the current flowing through the cell is what causes the destructive electrochemical action that ultimately wears out the cell, the amount of current that flows for any given length of time is what determines the useful life of that cell. A battery that supplies a small current over a small duty cycle will last longest. A duty cycle is the ratio of on time to off time. The larger the current or the longer the duty cycle, the shorter will be the life.

As part of their charter for establishing battery standards, the U.S.A. Standards Institute sets drain/life requirements for battery types. Some of these are:

Cell Size	Current Drain (ma)	Life (hours)
N	1.5	275
	7.5	52
	15	24
AA	3	350
	15	40
	30	15
AAA	2	290
	10	45
	20	17
B	5	420
	25	65
	50	25
C	5	430
	25	100
	50	40
D	10	500
	50	105
	100	45

You can see that for each battery type, any significant increase in current drain drastically reduces useful life. In addition to this, these ratings are based on an operating temperature of 70°F and *no more than two hours of operation per day.* If the duty cycle is larger than 2 in 24 hours, useful life drops even more. Ordinary dry batteries of the types listed above are designed not to be used for more than 15 or 20 minutes at a time, to allow them to rejuvenate themselves between uses.

summary

□ The dry cell uses a thick paste as the electrolyte. □ Dry cells operate in a manner similar to wet cells. The electrodes interact with the electrolyte in such a way that a difference of potential is developed between the electrodes. □ The Leclanche cell is the most widely used type of dry cell. It has an output voltage of about 1.5 volts. □ The zinc container of the Leclanche cell serves as the negative electrode, and a carbon rod is used for the positive electrode. □ The electrolyte of the Leclanche cell is made from ammonium chloride mixed with starch or flour to make a paste. □ The zinc container of the Leclanche cell is usually amalgamated to reduce local action.

□ Better types of dry cells are made leakproof by encasement in steel jackets. The jacket keeps the cell leakproof even after the zinc container wears out and develops holes. □ Dry cells are made to standard sizes and shapes. □ Dry cells can be connected to produce various voltage and current ratings. □ A cell's ratings and life depend on its internal resistance.

□ Although dry cell batteries cannot be repaired as can wet cells, their operating life can be extended by rejuvenation. □ After rejuvenation a dry cell is good again for a short period.

review questions

1. Why is a *dry cell* so called?
2. What are the materials used for the electrodes and electrolyte of the Leclanche cell?
3. Draw a sketch of a basic Leclanche cell.
4. What is the output voltage of a Leclanche cell? Of a mercury cell?
5. If you see a white substance on a dry cell, what does it probably indicate?
6. How is a dry cell made leakproof?
7. Who establishes the battery standards?
8. Name four battery type styles.
9. What is *rejuvenation*?
10. Can a dry cell be rejuvenated over and over? Explain.

the secondary (storage) battery

Primary cells have serious limitations because they have short useful lives. The rejuvenation of the dry cell is only a temporary measure. The wet cell can be repaired, but because of this, it is delicate and is usually restricted to laboratory use.

The secondary cell was developed for a *long useful life,* so that it could be ruggedly built for portable applications. The basic difference between the primary and secondary cell is this: The primary cell converts the chemical energy built into it to electrical energy, and in doing so, slowly destroys itself. The secondary cell has no significant electrochemical energy at the start. The energy must first be *charged* into the secondary cell. Then, the cell *stores* the energy until it is used. This is why the secondary cell is also called a *storage cell.*

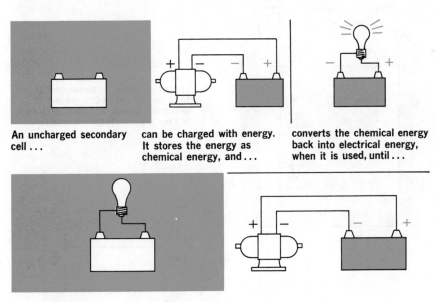

An uncharged secondary cell . . .   can be charged with energy. It stores the energy as chemical energy, and . . .   converts the chemical energy back into electrical energy, when it is used, until . . .

the cell becomes discharged . . .   Then it must be charged again

When electrical energy is taken from the storage cell, the cell is said to be *discharging.* When the cell is completely discharged, it no longer can supply electrical energy. But, unlike the primary cell, it can be *recharged.* Basically, the secondary cell *converts* the electrical energy to chemical energy when it is charged. Then, it *reconverts* the chemical energy into electrical energy when it discharges. The most popular storage batteries in use are (1) the lead-acid cell, and (2) various types of alkaline cells.

the basic lead-acid cell

The lead-acid battery can be obtained new, either charged or uncharged, and either with the electrolyte in (wet) or not (dry). For our discussion, let us start with a completely uncharged cell that has the electrolyte in it. The cell, then, consists of two electrodes, both made of lead sulfate ($PbSO_4$), and an electrolyte that is for the most part *distilled* (pure) *water*. There is some sulfuric acid mixed with the water, but in the uncharged state the amount is insignificant. The uncharged lead-acid cell, then, does not meet any of the requirements of a battery: its electrodes are *not* made of *dissimilar metals*, and its electrolyte will *not attack* one of the electrodes.

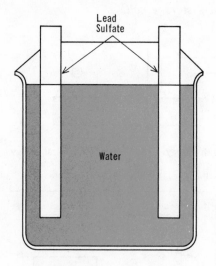

Lead
Sulfate

Water

The uncharged lead-acid cell cannot generate electrical energy because its electrodes are not dissimilar metals, and its electrolyte will not react with the electrodes

For the lead-acid cell to work, its electrodes must be made dissimilar, and its electrolyte must be made active

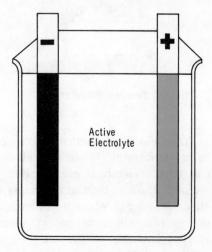

Active
Electrolyte

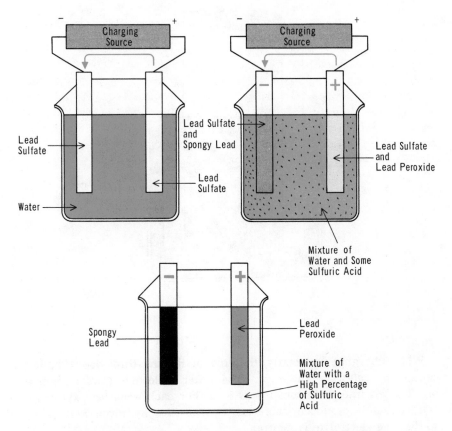

When the charging current changes the lead sulfate electrodes into spongy lead and lead peroxide electrodes, and produces a high percentage of sulfuric acid in the water, the storage battery is fully charged

charging

For the lead-acid cell to be able to deliver electrical energy, it must have two *different* electrodes, and an *active* electrolyte. This condition exists in the cell when it is charged by an electric current. Because of electrolysis, the water electrolyte breaks down and starts chemical reactions. One lead sulfate ($PbSO_4$) electrode changes into ordinary soft or *spongy lead* (Pb), and the other lead sulfate electrode changes into *lead peroxide* (PbO_2). At the same time, a good part of the water (H_2O) electrolyte becomes *sulfuric acid* (H_2SO_4). When this is done, the battery becomes charged: it has two different metals for electrodes and a chemically active electrolyte. The step-by-step action is shown on the following pages.

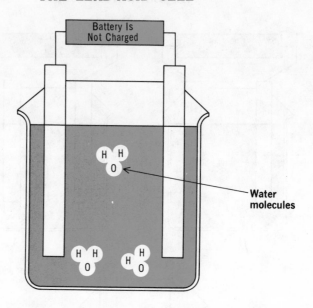

Water
molecules

electrolysis

When charging first starts, the current flowing through the battery causes *electrolysis* of the water. The water molecules (H_2O) begin to break down into their constituent ions. For each *negative* oxygen *ion* (O^{-2}) that is produced, there are two *positive* hydrogen *ions* ($H+$), so that the electrolyte is neutral.

Water molecules break
down into positive
hydrogen ions and negative
oxygen ions

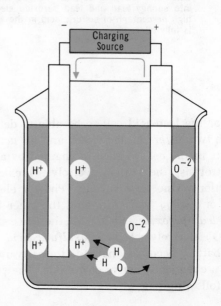

the negative electrode

After electrolysis has broken down the water (H_2O) into positive hydrogen ions ($H+$) and negative oxygen ions (O^{-2}), the attraction of the positive hydrogen ions breaks the lead sulfate molecules ($PbSO_4$) into positive lead ions (Pb^{+2}) and negative sulfate ions (SO_4^{-2}). The sulfate ions are attracted out of the electrode by the positive hydrogen ions. This leaves the positive lead ions behind in the electrode.

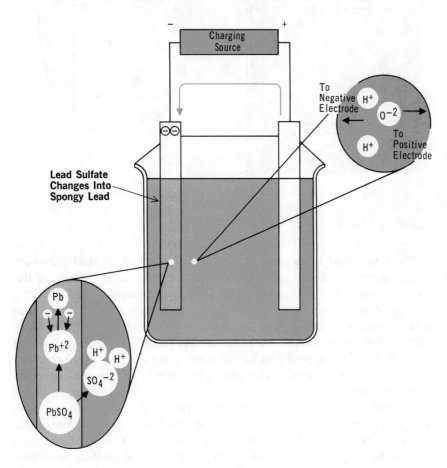

Electrons from the charging current are attracted to the positive lead ions and neutralize them, producing spongy lead (Pb). The action, then, is that the negative electrode begins as lead sulfate, gives off sulfate ions, and then becomes a mixture of lead sulfate and lead while the cell is charging; and continues to give off sulfate ions to become pure spongy lead when the battery is fully charged.

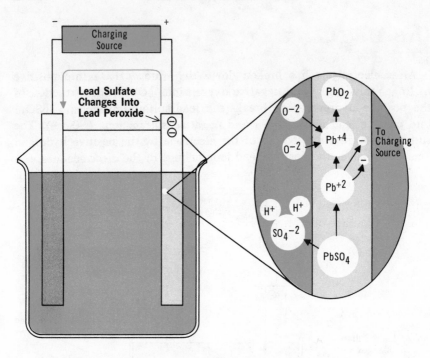

the positive electrode

The action that takes place at the positive electrode is similar to that which occurs at the negative electrode. The positive attraction of the hydrogen ions $(H+)$ in the water breaks down the lead sulfate $(PbSO_4)$ into positive lead ions (Pb^{+2}) and negative sulfate ions (SO_4^{-2}). The sulfate ions are attracted from the electrode by the positive hydrogen ions $(H+)$. This leaves positive lead ions behind in the electrode. This is the same thing that happened in the negative electrode, but there the lead ions were able to neutralize themselves by taking two electrons from the charging current.

Since the charging current is moving from the positive electrode, however, this cannot be done here. Instead, the positive attraction of the charging source pulls two electrons from the Pb^{+2} to keep the charging current flowing. This produces Pb^{+4}. The Pb^{+4} then attracts two negative oxygen ions (O^{-2}) from the electrolyte and combines with them to become neutral lead peroxide (PbO_2). The action, then, is that the positive electrode begins as lead sulfate, gives off sulfate ions and takes on oxygen ions to become a mixture of lead sulfate and lead peroxide while the cell is charging. The positive electrode continues to give off sulfate ions and to take on oxygen ions until it becomes pure lead peroxide when the battery is fully charged.

the electrolyte

Remember that when charging first started, electrolysis broke down each water molecule (H_2O) into two hydrogen ions (H^+) and one oxygen ion (O^{-2}). The positive hydrogen ions attracted negative sulfate ions (SO_4^{-2}) from each electrode. These combinations produce H_2SO_4, which is *sulfuric acid*. The positive electrode draws negative oxygen ions from the electrolyte. Therefore, as the charging of the cell continues, the electrolyte changes from water to a mixture of water and sulfuric acid. The longer the charging continues, the more the water is changed to sulfuric acid. When the battery is fully charged, the electrolyte contains a high percentage of sulfuric acid as compared to water.

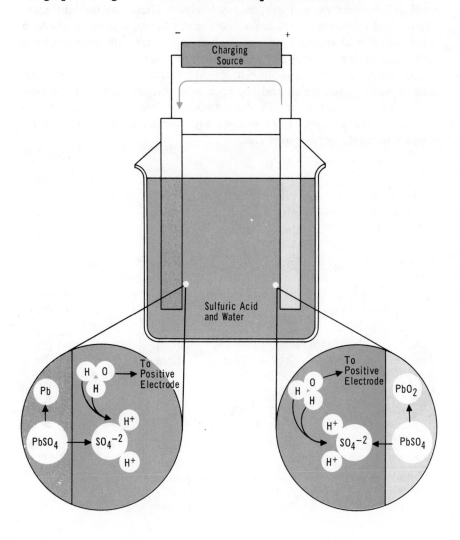

overcharging

When the lead-acid cell becomes fully charged, the negative electrode becomes pure spongy lead (Pb), and the positive electrode becomes pure lead peroxide (PbO$_2$). These electrodes no longer contain any sulfate ions (SO$_4{}^{-2}$) to combine with the positive hydrogen ions (H$+$) in the solution, and the positive electrode no longer absorbs the negative oxygen ions (O^{-2}). The hydrogen ions are then attracted to the negative electrode, and the oxygen ions are attracted to the positive electrode.

Electrons supplied by the charging current leave the negative electrode and combine with the hydrogen ions to produce neutral hydrogen gas bubbles. The negative oxygen ions give up electrons to the positive electrode and become neutral oxygen gas bubbles. These gas bubbles accumulate and rise as *gases* to leave the battery through *vent holes*. As a result, further charging does not change the water into more sulfuric acid. Instead, the water is lost as hydrogen and oxygen gases.

The water level will continue to go down until the ratio of sulfuric acid to water is too great, and the high acid content damages the electrodes. The escaping gases are dangerous, too, because they are explosive. When these gases are formed during overcharging, the electrolyte appears to "boil" as the gases rise.

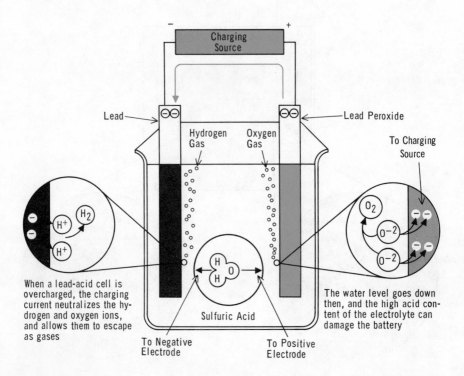

When a lead-acid cell is overcharged, the charging current neutralizes the hydrogen and oxygen ions, and allows them to escape as gases

The water level goes down then, and the high acid content of the electrolyte can damage the battery

summary

☐ A secondary cell has no significant electrochemical energy until it is charged. ☐ When a secondary cell is being charged, it is converting electrical energy into chemical energy. ☐ When the cell discharges, it converts the chemical energy back into electrical energy. ☐ A secondary cell is also called a storage cell, since after it is charged it stores the energy until it is used. ☐ Unlike the primary cell, a secondary cell can be recharged and used over and over.

☐ An uncharged lead-acid secondary cell has two lead sulfate electrodes and an electrolyte of mostly distilled water. ☐ The uncharged lead-acid cell does not meet any of the requirements of a battery: its electrodes are not made of dissimilar metals, and its electrolyte will not attack one of the electrodes. ☐ When an electric charging current is applied, one electrode changes into spongy lead, and the other into lead peroxide. In addition, most of the water electrolyte becomes sulfuric acid.

☐ Lead-acid cells should never be overcharged. ☐ Overcharging causes explosive hydrogen and oxygen gases to be produced. It also causes the electrolyte to become too highly acid, resulting in damage to the electrodes. ☐ If a lead-acid cell is being overcharged, the electrolyte appears to boil because of the rising hydrogen and oxygen gases.

review questions

1. Why are *secondary cells* often called *storage cells?*
2. What is the principal difference between a *primary cell* and a *secondary cell?*
3. From an energy standpoint, what happens when a secondary cell is charged? When it is discharged?
4. Does an uncharged lead-acid cell meet the requirements of a battery? Explain.
5. What is the composition of the electrodes and electrolyte of an uncharged lead-acid cell?
6. What is the composition of the electrodes and electrolyte of a fully charged lead-acid cell?
7. What is the purpose of vent holes in secondary batteries?
8. Why is overcharging dangerous?
9. How can overcharging be detected visually?
10. Can overcharging damage a secondary battery? Explain.

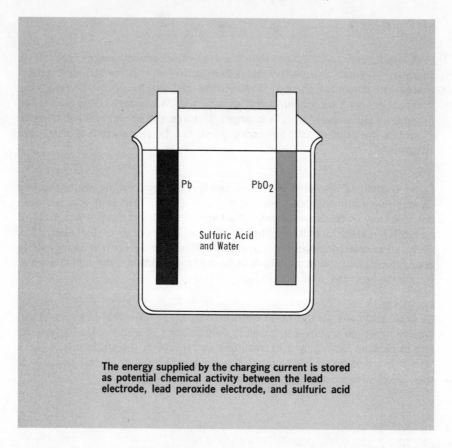

Pb   PbO₂

Sulfuric Acid
and Water

The energy supplied by the charging current is stored
as potential chemical activity between the lead
electrode, lead peroxide electrode, and sulfuric acid

the charged lead-acid cell

After the lead-acid cell becomes fully charged, one electrode is made of spongy lead (Pb), the other electrode is made of lead peroxide (PbO_2), and the electrolyte is diluted sulfuric acid (H_2SO_4). The cell now has the characteristics of a battery: it has two different electrodes, and an electrolyte that will attack at least one electrode. You may have noticed during the previous explanations, that while the electrodes were being *formed,* the electrodes merely conducted the charging current. They did not build up any charges of their own. As a matter of fact, the electrode atoms were kept neutral by the charging current flowing in the negative terminal and out of the positive terminal. This is the reason why the secondary cell does *not* store *electrical* energy. The energy supplied by the charging current is contained in the *potential chemical activity* of the lead electrode, the lead peroxide electrode, and the sulfuric acid.

developing a negative potential

As soon as charging current stops passing through the lead-acid cell, the sulfuric acid in the cell starts a *reverse chemical action* that is very similar to what happens in the primary wet cell. The electrolyte breaks down into positive hydrogen ions (H^+) and negative sulfate ions (SO_4^{-2}). The negative sulfate ions react with the negative electrode, causing the spongy lead (Pb) to give up two electrons and become a positive ion (Pb^{+2}). The negative sulfate ion combines with the positive lead ion to produce neutral lead sulfate ($PbSO_4$).

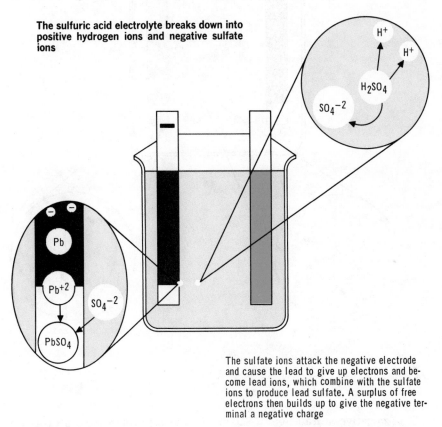

The sulfuric acid electrolyte breaks down into positive hydrogen ions and negative sulfate ions

The sulfate ions attack the negative electrode and cause the lead to give up electrons and become lead ions, which combine with the sulfate ions to produce lead sulfate. A surplus of free electrons then builds up to give the negative terminal a negative charge

In essence, the spongy lead negative electrode starts changing back to lead sulfate, but the two electrons given off by the lead ion remain free. The continued creation of $PbSO_4$ soon allows a surplus of electrons to build up in the negative electrode to give it a negative charge. When enough of a negative charge is built up, the sulfate ions are repelled from the electrode to inhibit further chemical action.

The positive hydrogen ions that are released by the sulfuric acid attract negative oxygen ions from the positive electrode. This leaves Pb^{+4} ions behind, which cause the electrode to build up a positive charge

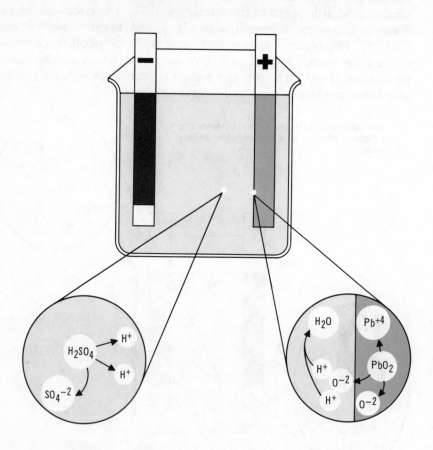

developing a positive potential

The negative sulfate ions (SO_4^{-2}) in the electrolyte also attack the positive electrode. Each lead peroxide molecule (PbO_2) of the positive electrode breaks down into two negative oxygen ions (O^{-2}) and one lead ion (Pb^{+4}). The oxygen ions are attracted into the electrolyte by the positive hydrogen ions (H^+). This leaves the Pb^{+4} ions behind; and when enough oxygen ions leave the electrode, it builds up a positive charge. When this charge becomes sufficient, the positive hydrogen ions are repelled from the positive electrode to inhibit further chemical action.

reducing the electrolyte

At the start of the electrochemical action, the sulfuric acid electrolyte (H_2SO_4) broke down into positive hydrogen ions (H^+) and negative sulfate ions (SO_4^{-2}). The sulfate ions combined with the lead ions of the negative electrode to produce enough lead sulfate so that a negative charge was built up. The positive hydrogen ions attracted enough negative oxygen ions from the positive electrode so that a positive charge was built up. The hydrogen ions and oxygen ions combined to produce water (H_2O), so that in the process of building a difference of potential between the electrodes, part of the sulfuric acid was changed back to water. The action stops when the lead-acid cell develops an emf of about 2.1 volts.

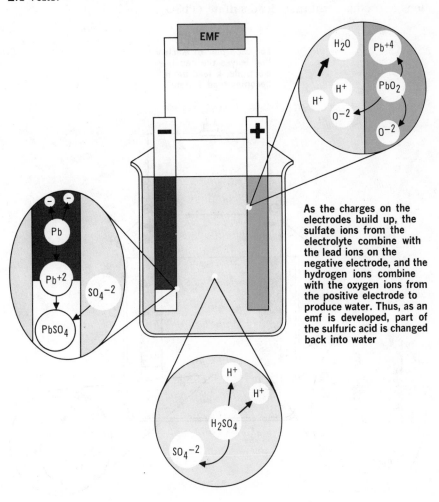

As the charges on the electrodes build up, the sulfate ions from the electrolyte combine with the lead ions on the negative electrode, and the hydrogen ions combine with the oxygen ions from the positive electrode to produce water. Thus, as an emf is developed, part of the sulfuric acid is changed back into water

discharging the lead-acid cell

When the lead-acid cell is connected to a circuit to supply current, the chemical action that produced the emf is continued to replace the electrons that leave the negative terminal, and remove the electrons that enter the positive terminal.

As electrons leave the negative terminal to go to the load, the charge on the negative terminal tends to diminish, allowing the sulfate ions (SO_4^{-2}) in the electrolyte to again react with the negative electrode. The lead atoms of the electrode give up electrons to replace those that have left, and become Pb^{+2} ions. These ions combine with the sulfate ions to produce still more lead sulfate ($PbSO_4$).

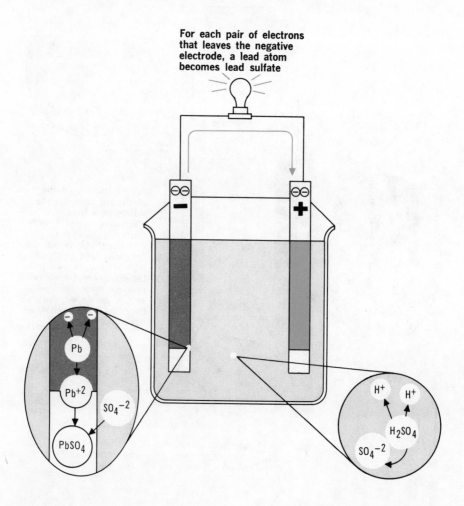

For each pair of electrons that leaves the negative electrode, a lead atom becomes lead sulfate

discharging
the lead-acid cell (cont.)

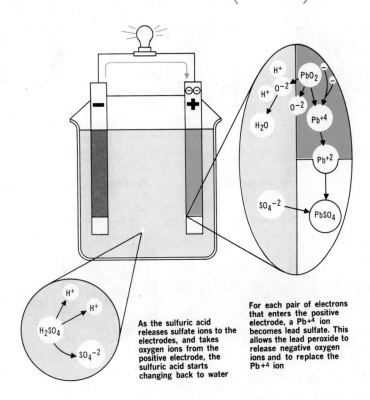

As the sulfuric acid releases sulfate ions to the electrodes, and takes oxygen ions from the positive electrode, the sulfuric acid starts changing back to water

For each pair of electrons that enters the positive electrode, a Pb^{+4} ion becomes lead sulfate. This allows the lead peroxide to release negative oxygen ions and to replace the Pb^{+4} ion

Whenever two electrons leave the negative electrode to go to the load, two electrons are attracted from the load into the positive electrode. These electrons combine with a Pb^{+4} ion, changing it to a Pb^{+2} ion. The Pb^{+2} ion then combines with a negative sulfate ion (SO_4^{-2}) from the electrolyte to deposit lead sulfate on the positive electrode. But the loss of a Pb^{+4} ion to the electrode causes another lead peroxide atom (PbO_2) to break up and give off two oxygen ions (O^{-2}) to the hydrogen ions in the electrolyte. This leaves another Pb^{+4} ion behind to take the place of the one that changed to Pb^{+2} and combined to produce lead sulfate.

In the process of the cell supplying current, the electrolyte gave up more sulfate ions, and absorbed more oxygen ions, so that still more sulfuric acid was changed to water.

While it is supplying current, the emf of the lead-acid cell drops to about 2 volts.

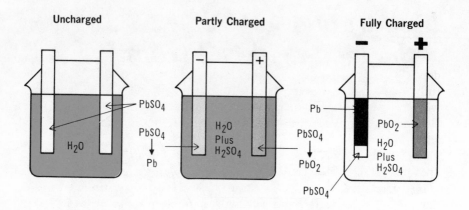

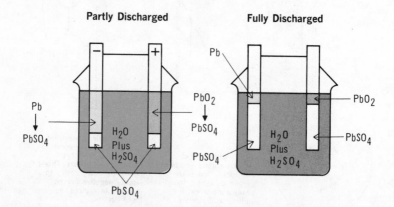

the discharged lead-acid cell

You can see that as the lead-acid cell continues to supply current, the spongy lead (Pb) negative electrode slowly changes into lead sulfate ($PbSO_4$). In a similar manner, the lead peroxide (PbO_2) positive electrode also slowly changes into lead sulfate. And the sulfuric acid in the electrolyte slowly changes into water. As the cell continues to discharge, both electrodes become mostly lead sulfate, and the electrolyte contains very little sulfuric acid. The cell, then, cannot generate sufficient emf, or supply sufficient current to be used; it is then *discharged*. But it can again be charged until the electrodes become spongy lead (Pb) and lead peroxide (PbO_2), and the electrolyte contains more sulfuric acid. It will work again until discharged, but can be used over and over again by periodic *recharging*. The lead-acid cell is considered discharged when its emf drops to 1.75 volts.

specific gravity

You learned that the chemical nature of the electrolyte actually depends on the state of charge that the cell is in. When the cell is fully charged, the electrolyte has a high content of sulfuric acid; and when the cell is discharged, there is very little sulfuric acid in the electrolyte. Therefore, the electrolyte could be tested to determine the state of charge of the cell. To do this chemically would be difficult; but it can be done simply by measuring the *specific gravity* of the electrolyte. Specific gravity is the ratio of the density of a substance to that of water.

Not all materials or liquids have the same *density*. Sulfuric acid is more dense than water, and so also is a mixture of sulfuric acid and water. And, the more acid there is mixed with the water, the more dense the electrolyte would be. The density could be checked by seeing how a *hydrometer* floated in the electrolyte. It would float higher in a dense liquid than it would in a thin liquid.

A syringe draws some of the electrolyte into the hydrometer, and a floating bulb gives indexed readings that show its depth of float. A specific gravity of 1.280 shows a fully charged battery, and a reading of 1.110 shows a discharged battery. The specific gravity of pure water is 1.0. Remember, though, that the density of sulfuric acid changes with temperature, and so its specific gravity is different at different temperatures. Most manufacturers rate their cell readings at 80°F. A good hydrometer will include a thermometer to check the electrolyte temperature, and give compensating adjustments for each 10 degrees of deviation.

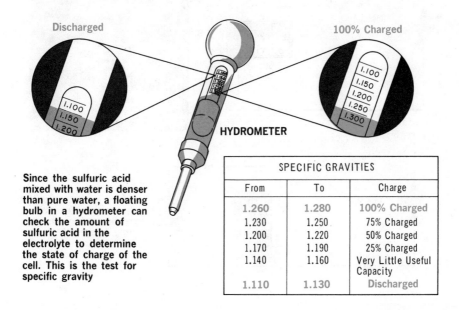

Since the sulfuric acid mixed with water is denser than pure water, a floating bulb in a hydrometer can check the amount of sulfuric acid in the electrolyte to determine the state of charge of the cell. This is the test for specific gravity

SPECIFIC GRAVITIES		
From	To	Charge
1.260	1.280	100% Charged
1.230	1.250	75% Charged
1.200	1.220	50% Charged
1.170	1.190	25% Charged
1.140	1.160	Very Little Useful Capacity
1.110	1.130	Discharged

charging methods

Storage batteries can be charged in various ways. The two basic methods are by *constant-current* and *constant-voltage chargers*. Either method can also be used to give a *high-rate charge*, a *low-rate charge*, or a *trickle charge*. Regardless of the method used, the charging current must be dc. The constant-current method with a low rate is the safest way to charge a battery, but it takes the longest—about 16 to 24 hours with a charging current of about 10 amperes. The constant-voltage, high-rate charger is the fastest method, but it has a tendency to damage batteries that may not be in the best condition. The high current accelerates the chemical action which could deteriorate the electrodes and boil the water, making the electrolyte too strong. This type of charging begins with a current at 50 to 100 amperes, which decreases as the battery becomes charged. This is why this method is also called *taper charging*. A moderate charge can be given with this method in one hour, but a few hours are needed for a full charge. The trickle charger is used to provide a small current to a battery while it is being used, thereby keeping the battery fully charged while it is operating. This, though, has a tendency to overcharge the battery and damage it if charging is not accurately controlled.

A constant-current charger uses a voltage source set slightly higher than the battery voltage to get proper charging current

A constant-voltage charger applies steady d-c voltage to the battery, causing a very high initial charging current

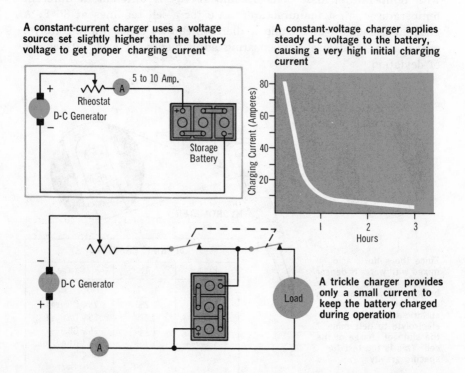

A trickle charger provides only a small current to keep the battery charged during operation

construction

As you learned when you studied the primary wet cell, the amount of current a cell can deliver depends on the surface area of the electrodes. In order to give the electrodes in the lead-acid cell a large effective electrode area so it can deliver large currents, each electrode element is made as a series of *plates*. Then the plates of the negative electrode and those of the positive electrode are *interleaved* so that the negative and positive plates are close together for efficient battery action. Thin sheets of nonconducting porous materials separate the plates to keep them from shorting.

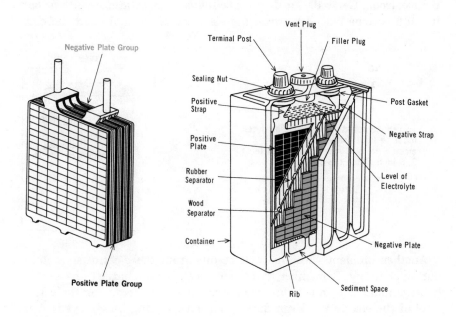

The set of plates for each electrode is connected by a *lead strap* that is attached to the associated lead terminal. The interleaved sets of plates are then usually encased in an acid-resistant molded container. Since the electrode materials are made of forms of lead, they are too soft to stay rigid. Therefore, the plates consist of grids, which have holes to hold the electrode materials. A lead-antimony alloy is generally used for the grid framework. A filler plug is provided at the top of the cell to allow the electrolyte level to be checked, and to allow water to be added when necessary. The filler plug generally has a vent hole to allow gases to escape.

disadvantages

You know that the operation of the lead-acid cell depends on the ability of the lead sulfate on the electrodes to be changed to lead and lead peroxide during the charging cycle. With a battery that is well cared for and *kept* fully charged, this is not a problem. But, when a battery is allowed to remain partially discharged for a long period, the lead sulfate tends to become hard and brittle; this is known as *sulfation*. The sulfated area of an electrode will not react properly with the electrolyte, and so the current capacity of the cell goes down. The sulfation process can continue until so much of the electrode area is lost that the battery becomes too weak to be useful. Also, the brittle sulfate can fall off the electrode. Generally, it drops to a *sediment* area at the bottom, but it could become lodged between the electrode plates and short the cell.

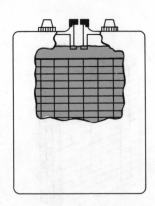

To reduce sulfation, the lead-acid cell must be kept charged, and the electrolyte level must be kept at least 3/8 inch above the plates

Another problem with this cell results from the electrolysis action during charging. Remember that when a cell is overcharged, the excess hydrogen and oxygen ions become gases and escape, reducing the water level of the electrolyte. Even during normal charging this happens, but to a lesser extent. Ultimately, the water content reduces to a point where the electrolyte level is too low, and the relative content of sulfuric acid is too high. This causes sulfation of the exposed areas of the electrodes to accelerate, and the overly strong electrolyte will attack the supporting member of the cell, which should not react with the solution. The electrolyte level must be periodically checked, and distilled water must be added to keep the level about 3/8 inch above the electrode plates.

The electrolyte in this type of cell also has a tendency to freeze in cold weather, particularly when the cell is not fully charged and the specific gravity of the electrolyte is low. The reason for this is that the electrolyte is mostly water, which freezes sooner than sulfuric acid. And when water freezes, it expands and buckles the electrode plates.

current ratings

Although the physical size of a battery has no effect on the emf the battery produces, it does affect the amount of current a battery can supply. The larger the area that the electrodes have, the more current a battery can supply. This is why storage batteries are made with interleaved plates. Both sides of each plate for a given electrode are available to supply current. The interleaving of plates also permits the electrodes to be close together. This reduces the internal resistance of the battery, so that high currents do not decrease the output voltage as much as they might otherwise.

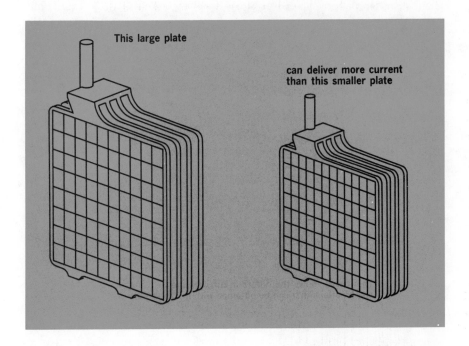

This large plate

can deliver more current than this smaller plate

Batteries are rated according to the amount of *current* they can supply in a given amount of *time*. The rating is given in *ampere-hours*. For storage batteries, the standard time used is generally 20 hours; so, if a storage battery is rated at 100 ampere-hours, it means that it will supply 5 amperes for 20 hours before its emf will drop to the discharged level, which is 1.75 volts per cell. But it can also supply more current for less time, or less current for more time; the ampere-hour rating is the same. For example, it can supply 50 amperes for 2 hours, or 4 amperes for 25 hours. The less current it supplies, the longer it will last.

current ratings (cont.)

In addition, the basic battery rating is given for operation at a temperature of 80°F. At low temperatures, the chemical activity of the battery slows down, and the battery cannot supply as much current. Therefore, batteries that are used outdoors, such as auto batteries, also are rated in ampere-hours for lower temperatures, such as 0°F.

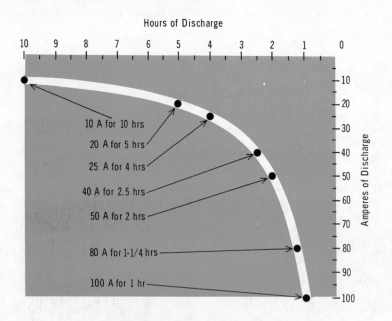

Hours of Discharge

10 A for 10 hrs
20 A for 5 hrs
25 A for 4 hrs
40 A for 2.5 hrs
50 A for 2 hrs
80 A for 1-1/4 hrs
100 A for 1 hr

Amperes of Discharge

This curve shows the different current-time combinations that can be obtained with a 100-ampere-hour rating

Some storage batteries, used for mobile lighting, are rated for four hours of operation, but this rating is still given as *ampere-hours*. Another older method of current rating, which is sometimes also given, is the maximum current that a battery can supply for *20 minutes*. This is just given in *amperes*, and should not be considered with the ampere-hour rating. It is known as the *20-minute rating*.

The ampere-hour rating is specified for *continuous* use over a certain period. Actually, if the battery is used only intermittently, it will last longer than its rating indicates, because it can rejuvenate itself between discharge cycles.

summary

☐ When the charging current is removed from the lead-acid storage cell, a chemical action occurs that is the reverse of that which takes place during charging. This chemical action causes a positive potential to be produced on one electrode and a negative potential on the other. ☐ When fully charged, the lead-acid cell has a no-load output voltage of about 2.1 volts. The output voltage drops to about 2 volts when the cell is supplying current. ☐ The lead-acid cell is considered discharged when its output voltage falls to 1.75 volts.

☐ The state of charge of a storage cell can be determined by measuring the specific gravity of the electrolyte with a hydrometer. ☐ A fully charged cell has a specific gravity of 1.280; a discharged cell 1.110.

☐ Storage batteries can be charged by either constant-current or constant-voltage chargers. Both types can be used to give a high-rate charge, a low-rate charge, or a trickle charge. ☐ The constant-current method with a low rate of charge is the safest charging method, but takes the longest. ☐ The constant-voltage high-rate method is the fastest, but can damage batteries that are not in good condition. This method is also called taper charging, because the charging current decreases as the battery becomes charged. ☐ Sulfation occurs when a lead-acid battery remains partially discharged for a long period. Effectively, sulfation causes part of the electrode to be lost.

review questions

1. What is the output voltage of a lead-acid cell at the instant the charging current is removed? Explain.
2. Explain briefly how a potential is developed on the electrodes of a lead-acid cell.
3. At what output voltage is a lead-acid cell considered discharged?
4. How is the specific gravity of the electrolyte related to the charge of a lead-acid cell?
5. What is the specific gravity of a fully charged lead-acid cell? Of a discharged cell?
6. Can ac be used to charge a storage battery?
7. What is *taper charging*?
8. What is *sulfation*?
9. Why must distilled water periodically be added to a lead-acid storage battery?
10. Why is it good practice to keep storage batteries fully charged at all times?

the alkaline secondary cell

The *alkaline* cell is much more expensive than the lead-acid cell, but it is still finding more and more use because it requires much less attention than the lead-acid cell and has a much longer useful life. Also, its electrodes are made of lighter metals, so that the cell itself is not nearly as heavy as a lead-acid cell. As you will soon learn, the electrolyte in an alkaline cell does not change chemically during charge and discharge, and so it does not tend to freeze as much as the electrolyte in a lead-acid cell. Because of this property, the specific gravity of the alkaline cell does not change, and so cannot be used as a method of checking the state of the battery charge.

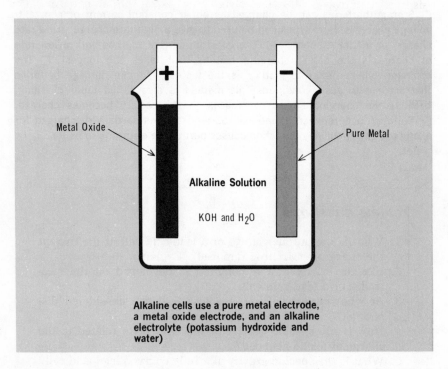

Alkaline cells use a pure metal electrode, a metal oxide electrode, and an alkaline electrolyte (potassium hydroxide and water)

Basically, the alkaline cell is so called because its electrolyte is an alkaline solution rather than an acid. This is just another type of chemical that reacts differently with metals than does an acid. The most common types of alkaline cells are the nickel-iron oxide cell, which was invented by Thomas A. Edison, the nickel-cadmium cell, and the silver-zinc cell. Each of these cells basically use a *pure* metal electrode, a metal oxide electrode, and an *alkaline* electrolyte of potassium hydroxide (KOH) mixed with distilled water (H_2O).

charging

Basically, the alkaline cell works similarly to the acid cell, in that the electrode materials change during the charge and discharge cycles. The electrolyte, though, does not change. All of the alkaline cells work in a similar manner.

To begin, you should know that a metal oxide is the metal combined with oxygen. The more oxygen atoms with which it combines, the more metal oxide molecules are present, and vice versa. When the alkaline cell is uncharged, both electrodes are metal oxides. Since the electrodes are not dissimilar, they do not produce an emf. But when a charging source is connected to the cell, the emf of the source produces electrolysis in the electrolyte. The electrolyte breaks down into an equal number of positive and negative ions. Only the negative ions, which are oxygen ions, react with the electrodes, so we can disregard the rest of the solution. The negative oxygen ions are repelled from the negative electrode, and are attracted to the positive electrode because of the polarities of the charging source. When an oxygen ion reaches the positive electrode, it repels electrons out of a metal oxide molecule, making it positive. The negative oxygen ion is then attracted to the metal oxide ion, and they combine to make the electrode more of an oxide. The electrons released by the oxide molecules are attracted out of the electrode by the charging source, to produce part of the charging current.

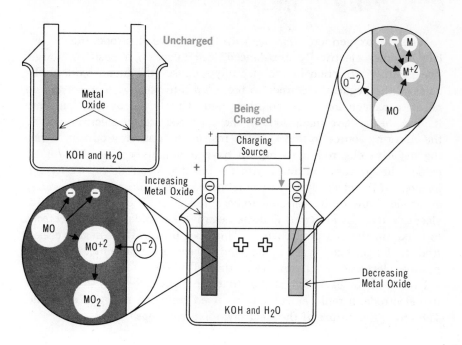

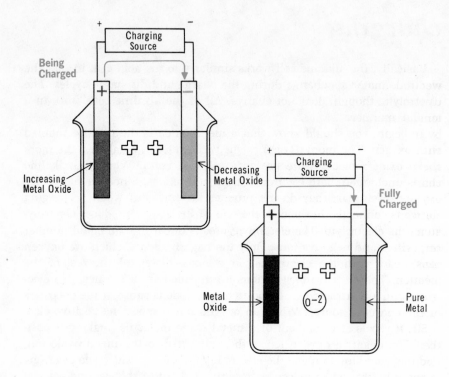

charging (cont.)

When an oxygen ion combines with the positive electrode, the electrolyte becomes electrically unbalanced, and takes on a positive charge. The positive attraction of the electrolyte causes the metal oxide molecules of the negative electrode to break up into positive metal ions and negative oxygen ions. The solution then attracts the oxygen ions into it. And the positive metal ions in the electrode attract electrons out of the charging source to make up the rest of the charging current. Since the negative electrode gave up an oxygen ion, it becomes less of an oxide. This process continues with the positive electrode taking oxygen ions out of the electrolyte to become more of an oxide, and the negative electrode giving up oxygen ions to become less of an oxide. The positive electrode releases electrons and the negative electrode attracts electrons to make up the charging current. This goes on until the negative electrode no longer has oxygen atoms, and so becomes a pure metal, and the positive electrode is fully oxidized: the cell is then completely charged.

Note that for each oxygen ion that the electrolyte gave to the positive electrode, a replacement was received from the negative electrode. Therefore, the nature of the electrolyte *never changes*.

how an emf is developed

You probably noticed that during the charging cycle, positive ions were produced in both electrodes. But in the positive electrode, the positive ions were neutralized when they combined with the negative oxygen ions. And in the negative electrode, the positive ions were neutralized by the electrons from the charging source. Therefore, while it is being charged, the alkaline cell does not build an emf of its own. It stores chemical energy, the same as the lead-acid cell, but as soon as the charging source is removed, the chemical action *reverses*. The negative oxygen ions in the electrolyte are no longer repelled by the pure metal electrode. Instead, they react with the electrode, and cause the metal atoms to give up electrons. The positive metal ions then attract and combine with the negative oxygen ions to produce a small amount of neutral metal oxide. The electrons that are freed accumulate in the pure metal electrode to give it a negative charge. When this negative charge is sufficient, the oxygen ions in the electrolyte are repelled to prevent further oxidation of the electrode.

Since negative oxygen ions have been taken out of the electrolyte, the electrolyte takes on a positive charge. The positive attraction of the electrolyte causes some of the molecules of the metal oxide electrode to break down into positive metal oxide ions and negative oxygen ions, and the oxygen ions are attracted into the electrolyte. This continues until the electrolyte again becomes neutral. The positive ions left behind in the metal oxide electrode build up a positive charge. The difference in potential between the two electrodes is the emf of the cell.

In the process of developing the emf, the pure metal electrode $(-)$ became slightly oxidized, and the metal oxide electrode $(+)$ became slightly less oxidized. However, since the oxygen ions that were given up to the negative electrode were replaced by those released by the positive electrode, the electrolyte did not change.

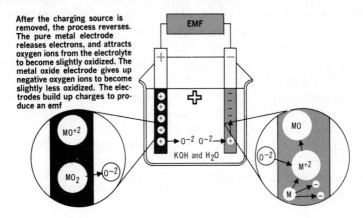

After the charging source is removed, the process reverses. The pure metal electrode releases electrons, and attracts oxygen ions from the electrolyte to become slightly oxidized. The metal oxide electrode gives up negative oxygen ions to become slightly less oxidized. The electrodes build up charges to produce an emf

the discharge cycle

Essentially, when the alkaline cell discharges, it just continues the process that built up the emf. Without current flow, the action stopped because the negative charge on the pure metal electrode prevented further oxidation. But when a load is connected across the cell, and current flows, electrons leave the negative electrode and enter the positive electrode. The number of charges on the electrodes decreases. But

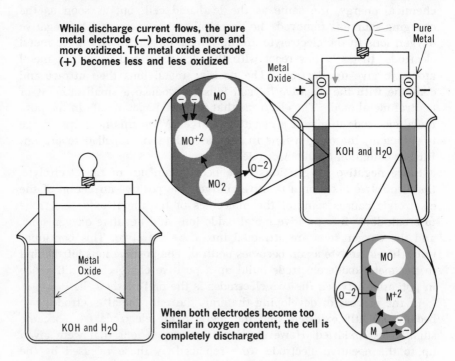

While discharge current flows, the pure metal electrode (−) becomes more and more oxidized. The metal oxide electrode (+) becomes less and less oxidized

When both electrodes become too similar in oxygen content, the cell is completely discharged

this allows negative oxygen ions from the electrolyte to again combine with the metal atoms in the negative electrode to release more free electrons to replace those that became part of the current flow. And, as a result, the metal oxide electrode releases oxygen ions to replace the ones given up by the electrolyte; it, therefore, creates new positive metal ions and negative oxygen ions to replace those neutralized by the current flow. Because of this, as discharge current continues to flow, the pure metal electrode starts changing into more of a metal oxide, and the positive electrode becomes less of a metal oxide.

When the cell is discharged, both electrodes become similar in oxygen content, and the cell is too weak to work. It must be recharged. But throughout it all, the electrolyte did not change; it merely exchanged oxygen ions between the electrodes.

typical alkaline cells

The oldest alkaline cell is the nickel-iron wet cell, called the *Edison cell*. It uses a nickel dioxide (NiO_2) positive electrode, and a pure iron (Fe) negative electrode. During the discharge cycle, the negative electrode changes into iron oxide (FeO_3) and the positive electrode into nickel oxide (Ni_3O_4). Fully charged, this cell produces 1.37 volts, which drops to 1 volt when it is considered discharged. Normal voltage is 1.2 volts. It is used mainly with railroad and telegraph signals, and portable lamps.

Alkaline cells can also be dry primary or secondary cells. A typical alkaline dry cell is the *nickel-cadmium cell*. It uses a positive electrode of nickel dioxide (NiO_2), and a negative electrode of pure cadmium (Cd). The cell also produces 1.2 volts, which remains relatively steady during discharge.

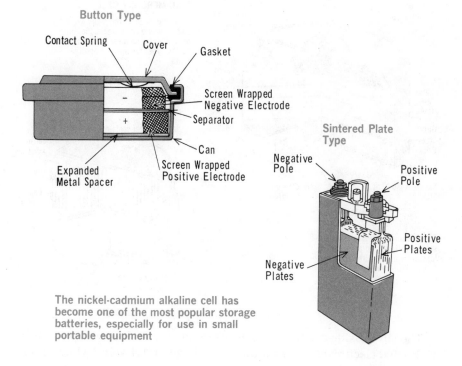

The nickel-cadmium alkaline cell has become one of the most popular storage batteries, especially for use in small portable equipment

More recently, the *silver-zinc cell* has a positive electrode of silver oxide (Ag_2O), and a negative electrode of pure zinc (Zn). It delivers 1.86 volts, which drops to 1.6 volts when discharged. It is also available as a rechargeable secondary cell.

alkaline dry cells

The zinc-mercury cell, commonly called the *mercury battery*, is another popular alkaline cell. It uses a negative zinc electrode, and a positive electrode that is a mixture of mercuric oxide and graphite. The electrolyte is a paste of potassium hydroxide and zinc hydroxide. The no-load voltage of this cell is 1.34 volts, which drops to between 1.31 and 1.24 volts when normal current is supplied. It is more expensive than the Leclanche cell but has a higher *constant current* rating. Special versions of the mercury cell can maintain such a steady voltage that they can be used as laboratory *voltage references*. Another variation of the mercury cell is a rechargeable secondary type, and yet another is the zinc-mercury dioxysulfate cell, which uses a zinc sulfate electrolyte.

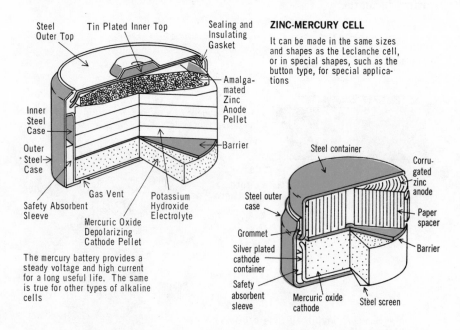

ZINC-MERCURY CELL

It can be made in the same sizes and shapes as the Leclanche cell, or in special shapes, such as the button type, for special applications

The mercury battery provides a steady voltage and high current for a long useful life. The same is true for other types of alkaline cells

The silver oxide-cadmium cell is a secondary cell. It uses a potassium hydroxide electrolyte. It has a no-load voltage of 1.4 volts, which drops to around 1 volt in use.

The zinc-manganese dioxide cell, with a potassium hydroxide electrolyte, is the principal alkaline primary dry cell that has been replacing the Leclanche cell in ordinary commercial applications. Like the Leclanche cell, it produces about 1.5 volts and is available in the typical popular Type N, AA, AAA, C, and D sizes.

summary

☐ Alkaline secondary cells use alkaline solutions as electrolytes instead of acids. ☐ Alkaline cells require less attention and have longer useful lives than lead-acid cells; however, they are considerably more expensive. ☐ The specific gravity of the electrolyte cannot be used to determine the state of charge of an alkaline cell. This is because the electrolyte does not change chemically during charging and discharging.

☐ An uncharged alkaline cell has two metal oxide electrodes and an alkaline electrolyte. ☐ A charging current causes chemical action within the cell which turns one electrode into a pure metal and the other into more of an oxide. ☐ When the charging source is removed, the chemical action within the cell reverses and causes a positive charge to be produced on one electrode and a negative charge on the other.

☐ One type of alkaline cell uses a nickel dioxide positive electrode and a pure iron negative electrode. This nickel-iron cell is also called the Edison cell. ☐ When fully charged, the Edison cell has an output of about 1.37 volts. ☐ The nickel-cadmium cell has a nickel dioxide positive electrode and a pure cadmium negative electrode. When charged, it produces an output voltage of about 1.2 volts. ☐ The silver-zinc cell has a silver oxide positive electrode and a pure zinc negative electrode. Its fully-charged output voltage is about 1.86 volts. ☐ The electrolyte of most alkaline cells is potassium hydroxide mixed with distilled water.

review questions

1. In an alkaline secondary cell, is there a relationship between the specific gravity of the electrolyte and the state of charge of the cell?
2. What are the advantages of an alkaline cell over a lead-acid cell?
3. Is an alkaline cell charged or discharged when both electrodes are metal oxides?
4. What is the function of the electrolyte in an alkaline cell?
5. What is an *Edison cell*?
6. In a charged alkaline cell, is the pure metal electrode positive or negative?
7. What effect does the charging current have on the electrolyte of an alkaline cell?
8. Why doesn't the electrolyte of an alkaline cell tend to freeze as much as the electrolyte of a lead-acid cell?
9. What is a *metal oxide*?
10. What electrolyte is used in most alkaline cells?

voltage ratings

Earlier, you learned that the voltage output of a battery depends only on the materials used for the electrodes and the electrolyte. The amount of material used or the physical size of the battery has nothing to do with the battery's voltage rating. Each specific combination of chemicals produces a specific emf. The only way that the voltage rating can be increased is by using more cells in series.

Batteries are rated with a *no-load voltage*. This is the electromotive force the battery delivers when it is *not* supplying current. When it *is* supplying current, the battery voltage *drops* slightly, up to 0.1 volt or so per cell. The *voltage under load* will drop even more with batteries that are more worn out. This is explained on page 6-24. For this reason, if you test a battery when it is not delivering current, the voltage reading you will get will not be meaningful. You should shunt the battery so that it will supply its rated current to see how much its voltage will drop. If the voltage drops considerably, the battery is worn out. Special *resistance- shunt voltage testers* are available to check storage batteries in this way.

The shunt resistor on this voltmeter causes a high current to flow, so that the voltage of the battery under load can be tested

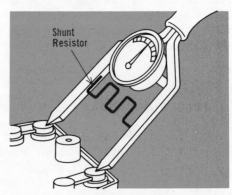

TYPICAL CELL VOLTAGE RATINGS

Type of Cell	Voltage Ratings		
	No Load	With a Load	Discharge Level
Copper-zinc-sulfuric acid, primary wet cell	1.08	1.008	About 0.8
Carbon-zinc-chromic acid, primary wet cell	2.0	1.9	About 1.7
Carbon-zinc-ammonium chloride, primary dry cell (Leclanche cell)	1.5	1.4	About 1.2
Mercury-zinc-potassium hydroxide, primary dry cell (mercury cell)	1.34	1.31 to 1.24	About 1.0
Lead-acid storage cell	2.1	2.0	About 1.75
Nickel-iron, alkaline storage cell (Edison cell)	1.37	1.3	About 1.0
Nickel-cadmium, alkaline storage cell	1.3	1.2	About 1.0
Silver-zinc, alkaline storage cell	1.95	1.86	About 1.6

other voltaic cells

For the most part, the battery relies on the chemical energy of the electrolyte to cause the electrodes to build up charges. You learned in Volume 1, though, that other forms of energy can be used to produce electric charges. The type of energy most commonly used is magnetism. The devices that produce electrical energy with magnetism fall into a category referred to as d-c and a-c generators, which are explained in the latter part of this volume.

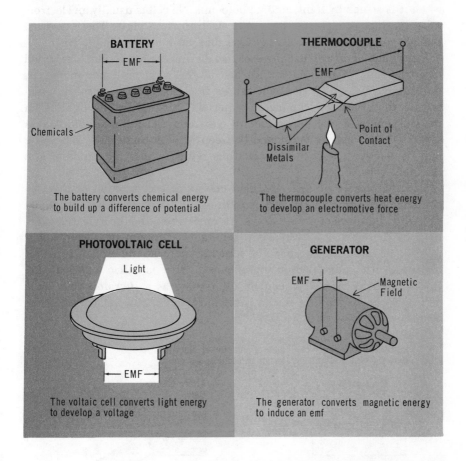

BATTERY

The battery converts chemical energy to build up a difference of potential

THERMOCOUPLE

The thermocouple converts heat energy to develop an electromotive force

PHOTOVOLTAIC CELL

The voltaic cell converts light energy to develop a voltage

GENERATOR

The generator converts magnetic energy to induce an emf

Light and heat can also be used by power sources to generate an emf. Sources that use light are known as *photovoltaic cells,* and those that use heat are called *thermoelectric cells.* An emf can also be generated by the triboelectric and piezoelectric effects, but these effects are not usually used in power sources.

photovoltaic and thermoelectric cells

The photovoltaic cell is one of three major categories of photocells. There are also *photoconductive* and *photoemissive* cells. These two types, though, are not power sources. They must be energized by a ·power source before they can work. The photoconductive cell is basically a variable resistive device that permits more current to flow in a circuit when it is struck by light; and a photoemissive cell is usually an electron tube that has an element that emits electrons to a plate. These devices, though, are not voltaic cells because they do not produce an emf.

The *photovoltaic* cell usually uses two dissimilar semiconductors joined together. And when light strikes one of the semiconductor materials, the energy released by the light causes free electrons to cross the junction to the other semiconductor material. Thus, while the light is on the cell, one side of it has a lack of electrons and the other side has a surplus; so an emf is developed between the two materials. When the light is removed, though, the electrons return across the junction and the emf drops to zero.

The *thermoelectric* cell uses heat energy at the junction of two dissimilar metals to cause electrons to cross the junction. Like the photocell, the thermoelectric cell loses its emf when the heat is removed. Both of these types of cells only generate a fraction of a volt, but a number of them can be added in series to increase the emf. A series of thermoelectric cells piled on top of one another is called a *thermopile*. One thermoelectric cell is usually referred to as a *thermocouple*. Lead telluride and germanium silicon perform exceptionally well as a thermocouple.

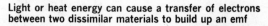

Light or heat energy can cause a transfer of electrons between two dissimilar materials to build up an emf

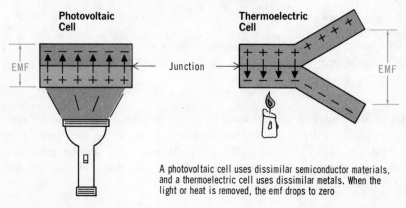

A photovoltaic cell uses dissimilar semiconductor materials, and a thermoelectric cell uses dissimilar metals. When the light or heat is removed, the emf drops to zero

solar cells

You can see that the basic photovoltaic and thermoelectric cells are limited in their usefulness as power sources because they lose their emf when the heat or light energy disappears. By themselves, these types of cells are usually used as *signal* sources, not as power sources. But, when they are combined with chemical storage cells, they become good power sources. This is generally the way *solar cells*, which are used in portable radios and artificial satellites, make use of the sun's energy.

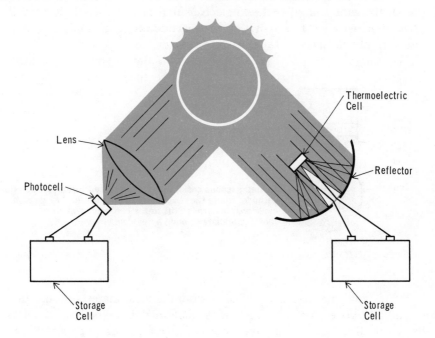

A solar cell uses photovoltaic or thermoelectric cells as primary cells to keep a storage cell charged

The photovoltaic and thermoelectric cells act as primary sources that keep a secondary cell charged. Then, as the emf of the primary cells fades when the sun goes down, the secondary cell continues to supply power. The secondary cell is repeatedly recharged whenever the sun's rays strike the primary cells. The photovoltaic cell uses the light energy of the sun directly, but the thermoelectric cell uses the heat from the sun's rays. Lenses of various types are used to concentrate the rays to make the cells more effective, and a number of cells are connected in series to produce the proper emf.

thermionic generator

The *thermionic generator* is one of the more sophisticated developments resulting from our space program research to produce more
reliable electrical sources.

A typical example of a thermionic generator is the *cesium cell*.
Cesium is a metal that liquifies easily at a little more than room temperature, and also boils over and becomes gaseous at much lower
temperatures than other metals. In addition to this, cesium atoms have
six shells, with a single valence electron that is so loosely held in orbit
that it is easily set free. For this reason, cesium compounds are often
used in photocells.

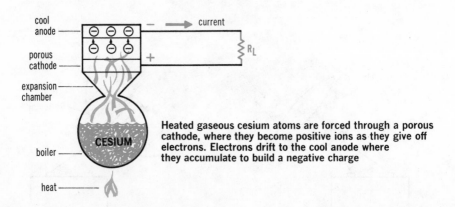

Heated gaseous cesium atoms are forced through a porous
cathode, where they become positive ions as they give off
electrons. Electrons drift to the cool anode where
they accumulate to build a negative charge

These same characteristics make cesium the ideal material to use in a
thermionic generator. The cesium is contained in a boiler, which is
heated until the cesium liquifies and boils. Hot cesium vapors rise into
an expansion chamber and a high vapor pressure builds there. The
cesium gas heats a porous cathode, and high energy cesium atoms are
forced through the cathode into a vacuum chamber. The high energy
atoms give off their valence electrons, and the positive cesium ions form
a positive space charge on the cathode. The electrons drift to the cool
anode where they accumulate and give off their excess energy. The
anode of the cesium cell then takes on a negative charge, and the
cathode, a positive charge.

When a load is placed across the cell, electrons flow from the anode
to the cathode. Electrons returning to the cell's cathode rejoin cesium
ions to neutralize them, but new high energy cesium atoms release
electrons to continue the current flow.

The disadvantage of the thermionic generator is, of course, the heating equipment required.

magnetohydrodynamic generator

The *magnetohydrodynamic generator* is another example of America's space-program efforts to produce new, more reliable electrical sources.

This type of generator also uses high energy *plasma* (ionized gas) as the basic energy source. But in this case the plasma is made to interact with a magnetic field to produce the desired electrical charges. A highly conductive plasma is used to provide the source of free electrons.

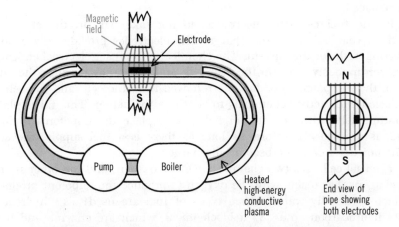

In the magnetohydrodynamic generator, free electrons in the fast-moving plasma are diverted by the magnetic field to the negative electrode for delivery to an electrical circuit. The electrons return to the other electrode to re-enter the plasma stream

The plasma is heated to ionization and pumped in a closed loop so that the ionized gases and free electrons circulate rapidly around the plumbing and through a magnetic field set up by a pair of permanent magnet poles. On either side of the plasma path within the magnetic field are electrodes. As the plasma passes through the field, free electrons are driven at right angles to the field and collect on the negative electrode. When a load is connected between the electrodes, these electrons flow in the circuit around to the positive electrode where they re-enter the flowing plasma stream. The hotter the plasma, the more free electrons there will be available, and the faster the plasma travels through the magnetic field, the greater the accumulation of electrons on the negative electrode.

For proper operation, the magnetic field, plasma flow, and the electrodes must all be at right angles to one another.

You can see that the magnetohydrodynamic generator also requires a good deal of auxiliary equipment.

the fuel cell

The fuel cell is one of the more promising developments of America's space program. Essentially, the fuel cell utilizes the basic principles of the battery cells you studied earlier, but arranges to have a continuous chemical supply to prevent the major disadvantage of the ordinary battery cell. The ordinary battery cell continues to discharge until either the chemical activity of the electrolyte and electrodes becomes impotent, or the electrodes deteriorate. The battery cell, then, has to be recharged or replaced.

In the fuel cell, the electrodes do not take part in the chemical activity that builds up the charge. The electrodes provide only a conducting path for the current. The chemicals that react electrochemically are continuously fed into the fuel cell, and after they produce the current, their impotent products are removed from the cell, and the cell is refueled with active chemicals to continue the action. This takes place continuously, with potent fuel fed in to replace the impotent product that is drained. Therefore, as long as there is a fuel supply, the cell will not deteriorate or become discharged.

The fuel cell uses two chemicals. One is oxygen, and the other is the fuel agent that reacts with the oxygen to produce the impotent product, which is usually water. Three types of fuel are used: (1) hydrogen, (2) hydrocarbon, and (3) a biochemical, which are enzyme and bacteria waste products. At present, hydrogen works best, but it is expensive. The hydrocarbons—gasoline, kerosene, butane, or any other petrochemical—are cheaper, but their carbon content interferes with their activity. The biochemicals are the least reliable, but would be the cheapest. They require the most heat to function properly. You can see that, like the other sophisticated cells, the fuel cell requires plumbing, pumps, and heating equipment to function properly. And the waste product must be disposed of. Also, the flow of fuel must be regulated to match the power drawn by the flow of current. However, this type of cell shows great promise.

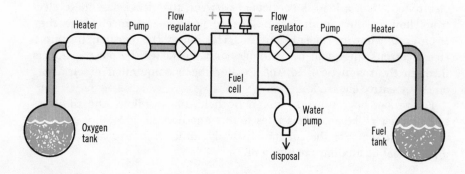

fuel cell operation

The fuel cell is constructed with the electrodes near each side of the cell. The chamber between the electrodes and the cell walls is where the oxygen and hydrogen (fuel) are fed in, each in its own chamber. The large chamber between the electrodes contains an alkaline electrolyte solution of potassium hydroxide (KOH), the same as the alkaline cells you studied earlier. Except for the thin electrodes and the plumbing, the fuel cell looks like the alkaline secondary storage cell.

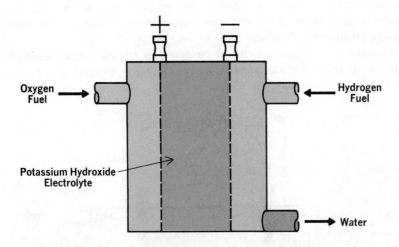

In the fuel cell, however, the chemical gases perform the same function as the electrodes in the earlier cell by reacting with the electrolyte electrochemically. The electrodes here are merely for electrical contact and to contain the chemicals in their respective chambers. The electrodes are made of porous membranes coated with a precious metal, such as platinum. They are porous enough to allow the electrolyte to seep through into each gaseous chamber just enough to react with the gases. The gas pressure keeps the electrolyte near the electrodes.

At the negative electrode, the heated hydrogen atoms ionize, giving off electrons, which accumulate on the electrode to give it a negative charge. These electrons flow to the load. This chemical action prompts a reaction in the water (H_2O) molecules of the electrolyte. The hydrogen atoms give off electrons to the oxygen atoms, creating positive hydrogen ions and negative oxygen ions. The negative oxygen ions are attracted to the positive hydrogen ions of the fuel and combine to produce water, which is drained off. New hydrogen atoms enter the chamber to replace the depleted hydrogen.

fuel cell operation (cont.)

This action leaves positive hydrogen ions in the electrolyte, so that the chemical activity of the hydrogen fuel tends to cause the electrolyte to build up a positive charge. At the oxygen chamber, the heated oxygen atoms ionize by taking electrons from the electrode. The negative oxygen ions are attracted to the positive electrolyte solution, and there react with the positive hydrogen ions to produce H_2O (water), which replaces that which was lost at the negative electrode. The other electrode, in the meantime, which had given up the electrons that ionized the oxygen atoms, has its electrons replaced by the current flow through the load. As the oxygen atoms are used to replenish the electrolyte, more oxygen is pumped into the chamber.

As you can see, neither the electrolyte nor the electrodes change or deteriorate from the chemical activity. Only the oxygen and fuel are used, but they are replaced.

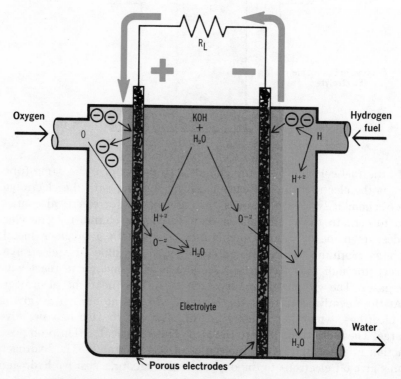

Ionized hydrogen fuel atoms provide the electrons for the current to flow through the load. The depleted hydrogen reacts with hydrogen ions from the electrolyte to produce water which is drained. The electrons from the load ionize the oxygen atoms which enter the electrolyte to replace those that were used. The electrodes and electrolyte do not change or deteriorate. Only the oxygen and fuel are used up

summary

☐ A *thermionic generator* uses heat and chemical activity to generate a charge. Cesium is ideal for this use because it becomes gaseous at lower heat than most other metals and ionizes easily. ☐ A conductive plasma passing through a magnetic field will provide electrons to suitably placed electrodes. This is the principle of a magnetohydrodynamic generator.
☐ In a fuel cell, the electrolyte and electrodes do not deteriorate. Chemical energy is supplied by oxygen and a fuel to produce the electrochemical action.

☐ A photovoltaic cell produces an emf when it is struck by light. When this light is removed, the emf drops to zero. ☐ A thermoelectric cell produces an emf when it is heated. ☐ A series arrangement of thermoelectric cells is called a thermopile. ☐ The solar cell consists of a photovoltaic or thermoelectric cell together with a chemical storage cell.

review questions

1. What is meant by the no-load voltage of a battery?
2. What is another name for a cesium thermionic generator?
3. What is a flowing ionized gas called?
4. How are the plasma, magnetic field, and electrodes in a magnetohydrodynamic generator placed relative to each other?
5. How does a fuel cell differ from a regular battery cell?
6. Name three kinds of fuel used in a fuel cell.
7. What are the disadvantages of a fuel cell?
8. Why are photovoltaic and thermoelectric cells generally not used as power sources?
9. What is a *solar cell*?
10. Two cells, each with an internal resistance of 0.2 ohm, are in parallel. What is the overall internal resistance?

generators

You have seen so far how three different forms of energy are converted into electrical energy. *Cells* convert *chemical energy* into electricity, *photovoltaic cells* convert *light energy* into electricity and *thermocouples* convert *heat energy* into electricity. You will now learn about devices that convert *mechanical energy* into electrical energy. These devices are called *generators*.

Basically, a generator produces electricity by the *rotation* of a group of conductors in a *magnetic field*. The input to a generator, then, is the mechanical energy needed to rotate the conductors. This energy can be supplied by gasoline or diesel engines, steam turbines, electric motors, flowing water, or even atomic reactors. In fact, anything that can be used to make a shaft rotate can be the input to an electrical generator. The output of a generator is the emf induced in the conductors as they move through the magnetic field. Since a generator requires a magnetic field for its operation, a generator might also be defined as a device that converts mechanical energy into electrical energy by means of a magnetic field, or by *magnetic induction*. The principles of magnetic induction were covered in Volumes 1 and 3. Actually, the magnetohydrodynamic generator works on the same principle, but uses a conductive plasma instead of wires.

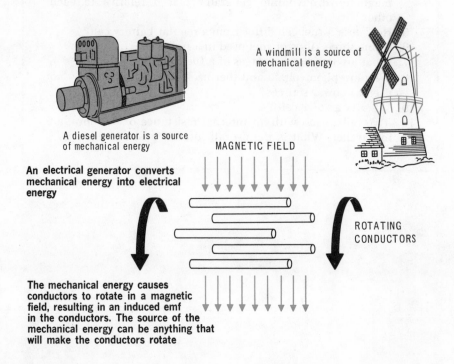

A windmill is a source of mechanical energy

A diesel generator is a source of mechanical energy

MAGNETIC FIELD

An electrical generator converts mechanical energy into electrical energy

ROTATING CONDUCTORS

The mechanical energy causes conductors to rotate in a magnetic field, resulting in an induced emf in the conductors. The source of the mechanical energy can be anything that will make the conductors rotate

generators (cont.)

Although generators are classified in many ways, there are only two basic types: *d-c generators*, which have a d-c voltage output, and *a-c generators*, which have an a-c voltage output. You will find that the principles of operation of the two types are similar in many ways.

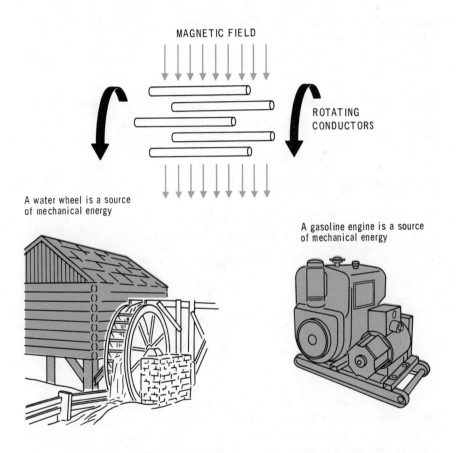

MAGNETIC FIELD

ROTATING
CONDUCTORS

A water wheel is a source
of mechanical energy

A gasoline engine is a source
of mechanical energy

From the standpoint of the total amount of power produced, generators are the number one electrical power source used in the world today. No other practical power source can produce the large amounts of electrical power that generators can. This does not mean, though, that generators are the best power source for all applications. They must be located at or near their source of mechanical energy, and unlike batteries, therefore, cannot be used in cases where portable power sources are required. In addition, they are often uneconomical for producing small amounts of power.

the basic d-c generator

A basic d-c generator has four principal parts: (1) a magnetic field; (2) a single conductor, or loop; (3) a commutator; and (4) brushes. The *magnetic field* can be supplied by either a *permanent magnet* or by an *electromagnet*. For now, we will assume that a permanent magnet is used. As shown, the magnetic field can be pictured as consisting of magnetic flux lines that form a *closed* magnetic circuit. The flux lines leave the north pole of the magnet, cross the air gap between the poles of the magnet, enter the south pole, and then travel through the magnet back to the north pole.

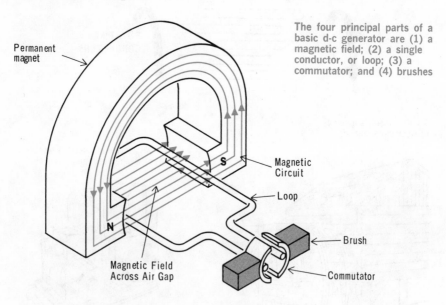

Permanent magnet

The four principal parts of a basic d-c generator are (1) a magnetic field; (2) a single conductor, or loop; (3) a commutator; and (4) brushes

Magnetic Circuit

Loop

S

N

Brush

Commutator

Magnetic Field Across Air Gap

The single conductor is shaped in the form of a *loop,* and is positioned between the magnetic poles. The loop is, therefore, in the magnetic field. As long as the loop does not rotate, the magnetic field has no effect on it. But if the loop rotates, it cuts through the lines of magnetic flux, and, as you learned in Volumes 1 and 3, this causes an emf to be *induced* in the loop.

You will learn that for each complete rotation of the loop, the amplitude and direction of the induced emf follows one cycle of a *sine wave.* As the loop rotates, therefore, a sinusoidal, or a-c, voltage is present at the ends of the loop. Since, by definition, d-c generators have d-c outputs, the a-c voltage must be converted to dc. This is done by a *commutator*. The d-c output from the commutator is transferred to an external circuit by *brushes.*

producing voltage

At this point, let us review some basic generator theory introduced in Volumes 1 and 3. This theory applies not only to d-c generators, which you are studying now, but to a-c generators as well.

Whenever there is *relative motion* between a magnetic field and a conductor, and the direction of motion is such that the conductor *cuts* the flux lines of the magnetic field, an emf is induced in the conductor. As far as generators are concerned, the *magnitude* of the induced emf depends mainly on the *strength* of the magnetic field, and the *rate* at which the flux lines are cut. The stronger the field, or the more flux lines cut in a given time, the larger is the induced emf. The direction or polarity of the emf is determined by the *left-hand rule* for generators. According to this rule, extend the thumb, index finger, and middle finger so that they all point at right angles to each other. Then, if you point the index finger in the direction of the magnetic field, and the thumb in the direction of motion of the conductor, the middle finger will be pointing in the direction in which current flows.

Applying the left-hand rule to the basic one-loop generator, you can see from the illustration that two emf's are induced in the loop as it rotates. These are induced on *opposite* sides of the loop, and have *equal amplitudes*. Their directions are such that they are in series with respect to the open ends of the loop. In effect, then, the amplitude of the voltage across the ends of the loop is *twice* the amplitude of the voltage induced in either side of the loop.

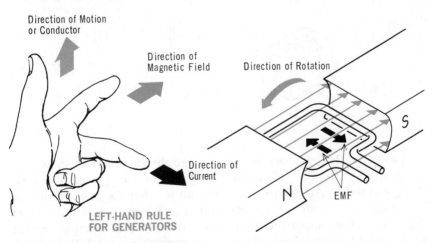

Direction of Motion or Conductor

Direction of Magnetic Field

Direction of Rotation

Direction of Current

LEFT-HAND RULE FOR GENERATORS

S

N   EMF

If the left-hand rule is applied to the basic single-loop generator, it shows that an emf is induced in each side of the loop, and that these emf's are in series

You can see that as the loop rotates, the side now moving upward will be moving downward, and vice versa. So the polarity of the induced emf in each side will also reverse

polarities

You have learned that electron current flows from negative to positive in a circuit. However, the generator in itself is not a circuit. It is a power source. So, if you think back to what you learned in Volume 2, you should recall that electron current flow *inside* of power sources goes from positive to negative.

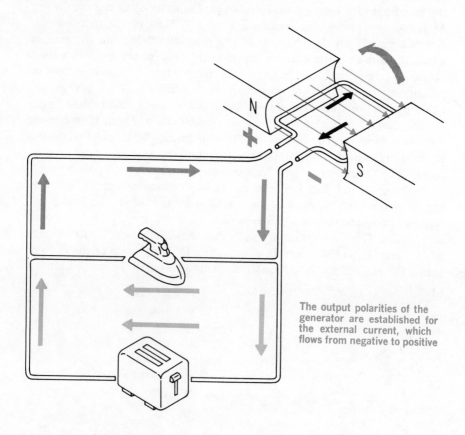

The output polarities of the generator are established for the external current, which flows from negative to positive

Essentially, the polarities are assigned to the generator to show how the electron current that is induced in the generator produces electric charges at the output connections. You can see that the induced current causes electrons to flow in a direction that produces an accumulation of electrons at one output terminal, and a deficiency of electrons at the other output terminal. Thus, the generator *polarities* are labelled according to the *charges* produced. Then, when a load is connected to the generator, current flows through the load from negative to positive.

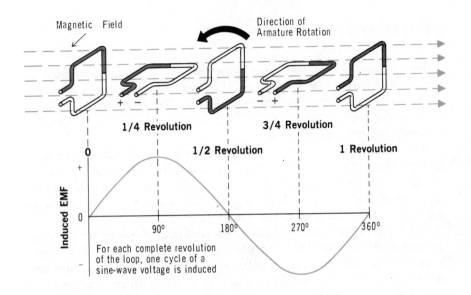

For each complete revolution of the loop, one cycle of a sine-wave voltage is induced

producing a sine wave

As was mentioned, the basic d-c generator produces a sine-wave output that is converted to dc by the commutator. Neglecting the commutator for the moment, you can see from the illustration that *one cycle* of the sine-wave output is generated for each *full rotation* of the loop. When the plane of the loop is *perpendicular* to the magnetic field, the sides of the loop are passing *between* the flux lines. Hence, no flux lines are being cut, so the induced voltage is zero. This happens twice during each full rotation.

When the plane of the loop is *parallel* to the magnetic field, the sides of the loop are cutting straight across the flux lines; so the induced voltage is *maximum,* since the rate at which the flux lines are being cut is maximum. This also occurs twice during each full rotation. However, in one position of the loop, the maximum emf is in one direction, while 180 degrees later, it is in the opposite direction, following the left-hand rule.

At all other positions of the loop, the sides of the loop are cutting the flux lines at an angle. It takes slightly longer for the wire to go from flux line to flux line, so less lines are cut in a given amount of time. Therefore, the induced voltage is somewhere between its maximum value and zero, becoming less as the angle of the loop increases from parallel to perpendicular. Then as the sides of the loop pass the zero-volt perpendicular position, they go in the opposite cutting direction, and an opposite emf is induced, which becomes increasingly greater until the loop is parallel to the flux lines. Then the process is repeated.

commutator action

The commutator, as you know, converts the a-c voltage generated in the rotating loop into a d-c voltage. However, it also serves as a means of connecting the *brushes* to *the rotating loop*. The way in which it converts ac into dc is directly related to its role of serving as a contact between the brushes and loop.

You will recall that the purpose of the brushes is to connect the generator voltage to an external circuit. To do this, each brush has to make contact with one of the ends of the loop. A *direct* connection is impractical, since the loop rotates. So instead, the brushes are connected to the ends of the loop through the commutator.

The commutator is made of two *semicylindrical* pieces of smooth conducting material separated by insulating material. Each half of the commutator is permanently connected to one end of the loop, and therefore the commutator rotates as the loop rotates. Each brush rests against one side of the commutator, and *slides* along the commutator as both it and the loop rotate. In this way, each brush makes contact with the end of the loop that is connected to the half of the commutator that the brush rests against.

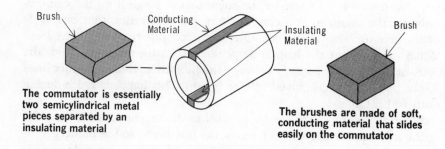

Brush   Conducting Material   Insulating Material   Brush

The commutator is essentially two semicylindrical metal pieces separated by an insulating material

The brushes are made of soft, conducting material that slides easily on the commutator

Since the *commutator rotates* while the *brushes* are *stationary*, each brush first slides along one half of the commutator and then along the other. This means that each brush is first in contact with one end of the loop and then the other. The brushes are positioned on *opposite* sides of the commutator so that they pass from one commutator half to the other at the instant the loop reaches the point in its rotation where the induced voltage reverses polarity. So every time the ends of the loop reverse polarity, the brushes switch from one half, or segment, of the commutator to the other. In this way, one brush is always positive with respect to the other. The voltage between the brushes, therefore, fluctuates in amplitude between zero and some maximum value, but it always has the *same polarity*. The fluctuating d-c voltage, then, is the output of the generator.

commutator action (cont.)

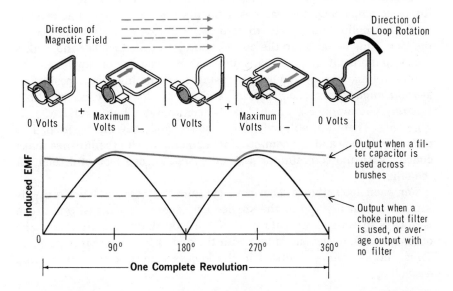

Direction of
Magnetic Field

Direction of
Loop Rotation

0 Volts

+
Maximum
Volts
−

0 Volts

+
Maximum
Volts
−

0 Volts

Output when a fil-
ter capacitor is
used across
brushes

Output when a
choke input filter
is used, or aver-
age output with
no filter

Induced EMF

0

90°   180°   270°   360°

One Complete Revolution

The action of the commutator and brushes in producing a fluctuating d-c output is shown on the following page. An important point to notice is that as each brush passes from one commutator segment to the other, there is an instant during which they contact both segments. The induced voltage at this instant is zero. If it were not, damagingly high currents would flow in the loop, since the brushes are effectively shorting the ends of the loop directly together. The position of the brushes so that they contact both commutator segments when the induced voltage is zero is called the *neutral plane*.

If you study the diagram, you will see that the left-hand brush is always connected to the side of the loop that is moving downward. This makes the left-hand brush always positive, as you can verify by the left-hand rule. Similarly, the right-hand brush is always connected to the side of the loop that is moving upward. This makes the right-hand brush always negative. So instead of the output voltage reversing polarity after one-half revolution, the voltage output for the second half revolution is identical to that of the first half. The commutator and brushes thus convert the induced ac into pulsating dc. If a filter capacitor were connected across the brushes, a more steady d-c voltage close to the peak amplitude would be produced. If a choke input filter were used, the output voltage would be the average level of the fluctuating dc. Even when no filter is used, the average is considered to be the output.

increasing the number of loops

As shown on the previous page, when no filter is used, the output of the basic single-loop generator is a fluctuating d-c voltage that reaches its peak amplitude and falls to zero twice during each full rotation of the loop. This variation in the output voltage is called *ripple,* and makes the output unsuitable for many uses. The variation, or ripple, in the output voltage can be reduced by using *two* rotating loops, positioned at *right angles* to each o·her. Each end of both loops is connected to a *separate* commutator segment, so the commutator has a total of *four* *segments.* There are still only two brushes, and they are positioned so that as the loops and the commutator segments rotate, the brushes make contact with the commutator segments first for one loop and then for the other.

For each loop, the brushes and commutator segments perform the same function they do in the single-loop generator. That is, one brush is always in contact with the end of the loop that is negative, and the other brush is always in contact with the end of the loop that is positive. Thus, the a-c voltage induced in the loop is converted to a fluctuating d-c voltage.

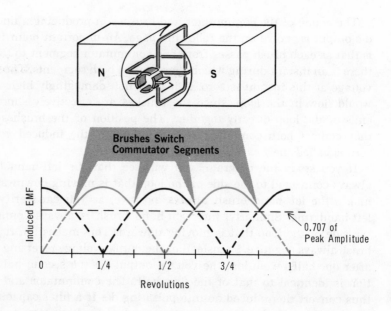

The voltages induced in each loop are equal, but 90° out of phase. When the loops reach the point in their rotation where their voltages are 0.707 of peak, the brushes switch from the commutator segment for the loop with the decreasing voltage to the loop with the increasing voltage

increasing
the number of loops (cont.)

There is one important difference in the two-loop generator, however. It is that one loop is always 90 degrees of rotation behind the other. So when the voltage in one loop is *decreasing,* the voltage in the other is *increasing,* and vice versa. And the position of the brushes is such that as the loops and commutator rotate, the brushes are always in contact with the commutator segments of the loop that has the *greatest* induced voltage. As the voltage in one loop drops below the voltage in the other loop, the brushes pass from the commutator segments of the loop with the decreasing voltage to the segments of the loop with the increasing voltage. This switching occurs *four* times during each full rotation of the two loops, and because of it, the generator output voltage, which appears between the two brushes, never falls below a value 0.707 times the peak amplitude of the voltage induced in either loop. This d-c output needs less filtering than the single-loop generator.

You should notice here that although the use of two *separate* loops decreases the fluctuation in the output voltage, it has no effect on the peak output voltage. The average output, though, is higher.

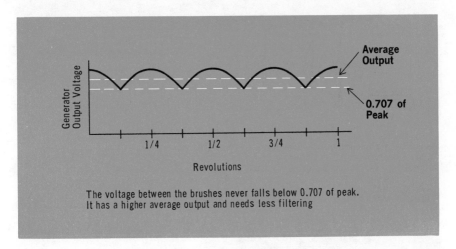

The voltage between the brushes never falls below 0.707 of peak.
It has a higher average output and needs less filtering

You have seen how by using two separate loops instead of one, the ripple in the generator output voltage can be reduced. By using more and more separate loops, the ripple can be further reduced, and the output voltage of the generator made very nearly *steady* dc. Little or no filtering would then be needed, and the average output would be almost the peak voltage.

increasing
the number of loops (cont.)

For every separate loop that is added, *two* more commutator segments must also be added; one for each end of the loop. Thus, there is always a *two-to-one ratio* between the number of commutator segments and the number of separate loops. Four segments are needed for two loops, six segments for three loops, and so on. Actual d-c generators contain many separate loops, and twice as many commutator segments. Therefore, if you were to count the number of segments on any generator, you know that there are half as many separate loops.

The output waveform of a generator having four separate loops is shown. Again, you should note that although increasing the number of separate loops decreases the variation between the maximum and minimum output voltage, it does not increase the peak output voltage, only the average.

In practical generators, the loops and the commutator together are usually called the *armature,* and sometimes the *rotor.* The armature, then, in this type of generator is the part that *rotates.*

Every additional loop requires two additional commutator segments

The commutator segments and brushes convert the induced a-c voltages into fluctuating d-c voltages, the same as the single-loop generator. However, the brushes are only in contact with the segments for the short period when the voltage in that loop is close to its peak value

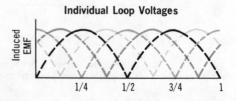

Individual Loop Voltages

Induced EMF

1/4   1/2   3/4   1

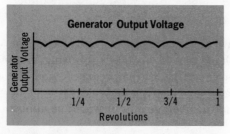

Generator Output Voltage

Generator Output Voltage

1/4   1/2   3/4   1

Revolutions

The average output voltage between the brushes is, therefore, close to the peak value of the individual loops

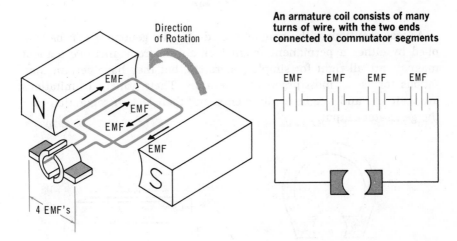

Direction of Rotation

EMF
EMF
EMF
EMF

N

S

4 EMF's

An armature coil consists of many turns of wire, with the two ends connected to commutator segments

EMF   EMF   EMF   EMF

The individual voltages induced in each turn are all in series, so their sum appears between the brushes

raising output voltage

In the basic d-c generator described, the output voltage amplitude is the same as that induced in each separate rotating loop, and is *very small*. You will recall that the amplitude of the voltage in each loop is determined by the *rate* at which the loop cuts the magnetic flux lines; and this, in turn, depends on the strength of the magnetic field and the speed at which the loop rotates. You might think, therefore, that the voltage could be increased by increasing the strength of the magnetic field or the speed of rotation, or both. Both of these measures, though, are impractical beyond certain limits.

Instead, the output voltage of a d-c generator can be increased to a usable level by having each rotating loop consist of *many turns* of wire rather than a single turn. These multiturn loops are called *armature coils*, or just coils. Each coil has two ends, and requires two commutator segments, the same as a simple one-turn loop. The total voltage induced in a coil, though is the *sum* of the individual voltages induced in each turn. The armature coils used in actual generators often have many turns, making possible high generator output voltages. You can see, then, that for a given magnetic field and speed of rotation, the *number of turns* in each coil determines the *amplitude* of the generator output voltage, while the number of coils determines the amount of ripple in the output.

producing the magnetic field

As was mentioned, the magnetic field of a d-c generator can be supplied by either a permanent magnet or an electromagnet. Permanent magnets are all right for simple generators, but they have certain limitations for use in most practical generators. Their principal limitations are their size and weight requirements, and their lack of regulation over the generator output.

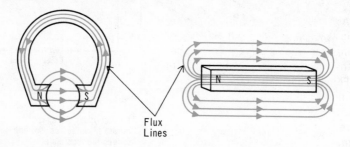

Flux
Lines

To provide magnetic fields of the required strength, permanent magnets must be relatively large and heavy

Since the strength of their magnetic field is fixed, they cannot provide any regulation of the generator output voltage

Electromagnets can produce much stronger magnetic fields than can permanent magnets of the same size and weight. Furthermore, electromagnets have properties that make it possible to regulate the generator output voltage to compensate for changes in load and speed. You will learn more of this later. Because of these factors, the use of permanent magnets in generators is limited. Most of the generators you will encounter will have their magnetic fields supplied by electromagnets. Those generators that do use permanent magnets are usually small and have low outputs. They are often called *magnetos*.

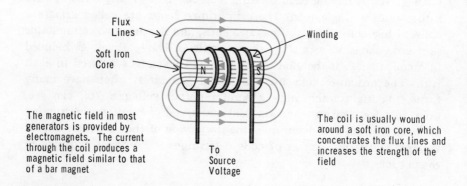

Flux
Lines

Winding

Soft Iron
Core

The magnetic field in most generators is provided by electromagnets. The current through the coil produces a magnetic field similar to that of a bar magnet

To
Source
Voltage

The coil is usually wound around a soft iron core, which concentrates the flux lines and increases the strength of the field

summary

☐ A generator converts mechanical energy into electrical energy by the rotation of a group of conductors in a magnetic field. ☐ Basically, there are two types of generators: dc and ac. ☐ A simple d-c generator consists of a magnetic field, a conductor in the form of a loop, a commutator, and brushes. ☐ The magnetic field of a generator can be produced by either a permanent magnet or an electromagnetic. ☐ Most generators use electromagnets, since they can produce stronger fields than permanent magnets, and also provide a means for regulating the generator output voltage.

☐ As the loop of a simple generator rotates, it cuts the flux lines of the magnetic field. As a result, an emf is induced in the loop. ☐ The emf induced in a single loop is in the form of a sine wave. ☐ The sine-wave voltage induced in the loop is converted to fluctuating dc by the commutator and brushes. ☐ For proper commutation to take place, the brushes must be positioned in the neutral plane. ☐ The amplitude variation in the d-c output voltage of a single-loop generator is called ripple. ☐ Ripple can be reduced by using more than one single rotating loop. ☐ Every loop requires two commutator segments. Thus, there is always a two-to-one ratio between the number of commutator segments and the number of separate loops.

☐ In actual generators, each rotating loop often consists of many turns of wire. These multiturn loops are called armature coils. ☐ The total voltage induced in each armature coil is the sum of the individual voltages induced in each turn. ☐ The number of turns in each coil determines the amplitude of the generator output. ☐ The number of coils determines the amount of ripple in the output.

review questions

1. What is the *left-hand rule for generators*?
2. What is the purpose of the commutator and brushes?
3. What is the *neutral plane*?
4. Which has the smaller ripple: a generator with two armature coils, or one with four armature coils?
5. If a generator has eight commutator segments, how many separate armature coils does it have?
6. What factors determine the output voltage of a generator?
7. What is a *magneto*?
8. Will increasing the number of turns in the armature coils affect the amount of ripple in the output of a d-c generator?
9. Does the number of armature coils affect the number of brushes required for a d-c generator?
10. What would happen if the brushes were not positioned in the neutral plane?

the field winding

The electromagnets used to produce the magnetic field of a generator are called *field coils*. In a simple generator, there are two field coils positioned so that their magnetic fields combine to form one magnetic circuit. As shown, the field coils are wound around cores, called *pole pieces,* that are part of the generator housing. The two pole pieces are separated by a space or gap into which the armature is placed. The closed magnetic circuit is from the "north" pole piece, across the gap to the "south" pole piece, and then through the housing back to the north pole piece. The generator housing, like the pole pieces, is made of material having good magnetic properties, so it helps increase the strength of the magnetic field. There is no electrical connection between the field coil and the pole pieces or generator housing. They form only a *magnetic circuit.*

The field winding supplies the magnetic field required by the generator. It is made up of the individual field coils, and is energized by a d-c voltage source

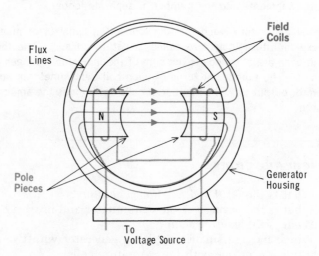

The strength of the magnetic field set up by the field winding depends not only on the physical construction of the field coils, but also on the current level applied to the winding. The greater the current, the stronger will be the field

The two field coils are wound in *series,* and so are energized by the same voltage source. This voltage source is dc, and as a result, the magnetic field produced by the field coils is always in the same direction. Both field coils together are called the *field winding.*

multiple field windings

The simple generator has two field coils, and therefore two poles: one north and one south. This is a two-pole generator. Many actual generators have *four poles, six poles,* and so on. No matter how many field coils there are, the total number of poles is always an *even number,* since for every north pole there must be a south pole.

One reason for having more than two field coils is that by increasing the number of field coils, or poles, the size and weight of the generator can be reduced while its output remains the same. In a two-pole generator, half of the flux lines must pass through the width or thickness of the armature core, which is a magnetic material. The armature core must be thick enough to prevent magnetic *saturation.*

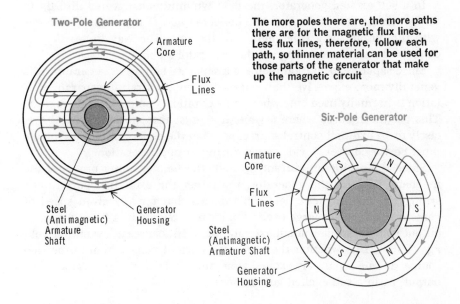

Two-Pole Generator

Armature Core

Flux Lines

Steel (Antimagnetic) Armature Shaft

Generator Housing

The more poles there are, the more paths there are for the magnetic flux lines. Less flux lines, therefore, follow each path, so thinner material can be used for those parts of the generator that make up the magnetic circuit

Six-Pole Generator

Armature Core

Flux Lines

Steel (Antimagnetic) Armature Shaft

Generator Housing

In a six-pole generator, only one-sixth of the flux lines have to pass through the thickness of the armature core in any one spot. But, since there is a series of flux lines, the total number is the same. The core can, therefore, be made substantially thinner and still pass the same total flux lines with little opposition. This also holds true for the generator housing, which serves as part of the path for the flux lines. The more poles there are, the thinner the housing can be. In effect, the more poles there are, the more paths the magnetic flux lines will follow.

Another reason for increasing the number of poles is that with certain types of armature windings, the output voltage of the generator can be increased. This is covered later.

exciting the field winding

Since the field winding is an electromagnet, current must flow through it to produce a magnetic field. For proper operation of a d-c generator, the magnetic field of the field winding must always be in the same direction, so the current through the winding must be dc. This current is called the *excitation current,* and can be supplied to the field winding in one of two ways; it can come from a separate, external d-c voltage source, in which case the generator is called a *separately excited generator;* or it can come from the generator's own output, in which case the generator is called a *self-excited generator.* The excitation source for separately excited generators can be a battery or another d-c generator. When a generator is used, it is called an *exciter.*

In a self-excited generator, the field winding is connected directly to the generator output. It may be connected *across* the output, in *series* with the output, or a *combination* of the two. The way in which it is connected determines many of the generator's characteristics.

Since separate excitation requires a separate battery or generator, it is generally more expensive than self-excitation. As a result, separate excitation is normally used only when self-excitation would be unsatisfactory. This occurs in cases where a generator must respond quickly and precisely to an external control source, or when the generator output voltage must be varied over a wide range during normal operation.

Since the excitation current through the field winding produces the magnetic field for the generator, the larger the excitation current the stronger is the magnetic field. This means that for any given speed of generator rotation, a large excitation current results in a high generator output voltage, while a small excitation current causes a low output voltage. This is true whether the excitation current comes from an outside source, as in a separately excited generator, or from the generator's own output, as in a self-excited generator.

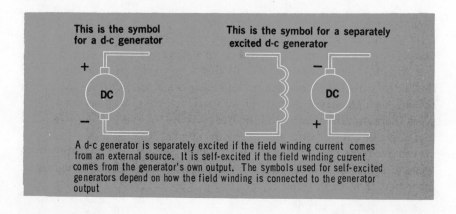

This is the symbol for a d-c generator

This is the symbol for a separately excited d-c generator

A d-c generator is separately excited if the field winding current comes from an external source. It is self-excited if the field winding current comes from the generator's own output. The symbols used for self-excited generators depend on how the field winding is connected to the generator output

series generators

When the field winding of a *self-excited generator* is connected in *series* with the generator output, the generator is called a *series generator*. The exciting current through the field winding of such a generator is the same as the current the generator delivers to the load. If the load has a high resistance and so draws only a small current from the generator, the excitation current is also small. This means that the magnetic field of the field winding is weak, making the generator output voltage low. Similarly, if the load draws a large current, the excitation current is also large, the magnetic field of the field winding is strong, and the generator output voltage is high. You can see then that in a series generator, changes in load current greatly affect the generator output voltage. A series generator is thus said to have *poor voltage regulation,* and, as a result, series generators are not recommended for fluctuating loads.

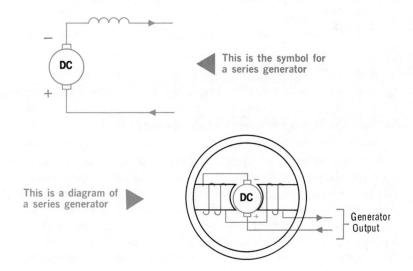

This is the symbol for a series generator

This is a diagram of a series generator

Generator Output

In a series generator, the field winding is connected in series with the generator output. Therefore, the same current that flows through the load flows through the field winding

The graph on the next page shows how the output voltage of a series generator varies with increasing load current. You will notice that as the load current increases, the output voltage also increases, up to a certain point. After that point, further increases in current result in a decrease in the output voltage.

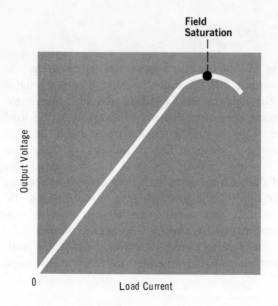

Field Saturation

Up to a certain point, the output voltage of a series generator increases with the load current

After this point, the voltage decreases with increases in load current

Output Voltage

0   Load Current

Since the output voltage varies with load current, a series generator has poor voltage regulation

series generators (cont.)

The point where the voltage no longer increases corresponds to the point of *magnetic saturation* of the field winding. This occurs, as you will recall from Volume 3, when the core material, which is the pole pieces in this case, is completely magnetized. The magnetic flux cannot increase any further, regardless of how much more the current through the winding is increased. The reason why the output voltage drops after this point instead of staying constant at its maximum value is because of the increased voltage drop of the field winding and armature coils. The voltage drop increases because of the increasing current, but the generated voltage stays the same. And since the output voltage equals the generated voltage minus the internal voltage drop, the output voltage must therefore decrease. Another reason for the decrease in the output voltage is that *armature reaction* increases. This will be described later.

A further disadvantage of the series generator, besides its poor voltage regulation, is that the field winding must be wound with wire that can safely carry the entire load current without overheating. This requires wire with a relatively large cross-sectional area.

shunt generators

When the field winding of a self-excited generator is connected in *parallel* with the generator output, the generator is called a *shunt generator*. The value of the excitation current in a shunt generator depends on the output voltage and the resistance of the field winding. Usually, the excitation current is kept somewhere between 0.5 and 5 percent of the total current drawn from the generator.

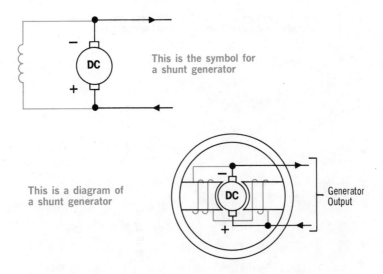

This is the symbol for a shunt generator

This is a diagram of a shunt generator

Generator Output

In a shunt generator, the field winding is connected in parallel with, or across, the generator output. The exciting current, therefore, depends on the value of the output voltage and the resistance of the field winding

The output voltage of a shunt generator running at constant speed under varying load conditions is much more stable than the output voltage of a series generator. However, some change in output voltage still takes place. This change is caused by the fact that when the load current increases, the voltage (IR) drop across the armature coil increases, and this causes the output voltage to decrease. As a result, the current through the field winding decreases, decreasing the magnetic field and thereby causing the output voltage to decrease even more. If the current drawn by the load is much greater than a shunt generator is designed to deliver, the drop in output voltage is extreme. However, for load current changes within the design range, the drop in output voltage with increasing load current is not too severe.

shunt generators (cont.)

The fact that their output voltage drops as load current increases, provides shunt generators with a *self-protective* feature. If the load should be suddenly "shorted," the output voltage would drop to zero. No excitation current, therefore, would flow through the field winding, so the generator would, in effect, be disabled.

The output voltage of a shunt generator drops gradually with increasing load current within its normal operating range

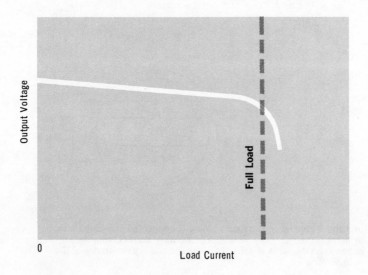

The output voltage drops drastically if the load current increases above the rated full-load value

The change in the voltage output of a shunt generator with changes in load current is also caused to some extent by a change in the *armature reaction,* the same as was previously mentioned for series generators. Armature reaction is covered later.

Compared to series generators, the excitation current in shunt generators is very small. Thin wire can, therefore, be used for the field winding. In actual shunt generators, the field coils consist of many turns of small-diameter wire.

compound generators

Both series and shunt generators have the disadvantage in that changes in their load current from zero to normal full-load cause their output voltage to change also. In a *series generator,* an increase in load current causes an *increase* in output voltage; whereas in a *shunt generator,* an increase in load current causes a *decrease* in output voltage. Many applications in which generators are used require that the generator output voltage be more stable than that supplied by either a series or a shunt generator. One way to supply such a stable voltage is by using a shunt generator with some form of *voltage regulation.* Voltage regulation of generators is covered later. Another means of supplying a stable voltage is by using a *compound generator.*

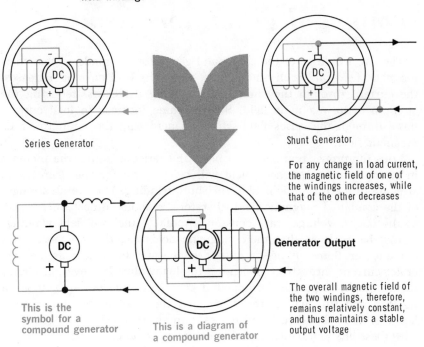

A compound generator has both series and shunt field windings

Series Generator

Shunt Generator

For any change in load current, the magnetic field of one of the windings increases, while that of the other decreases

Generator Output

This is the symbol for a compound generator

This is a diagram of a compound generator

The overall magnetic field of the two windings, therefore, remains relatively constant, and thus maintains a stable output voltage

A compound generator has a field winding connected in *parallel* with the generator output, the same as a shunt generator; and it also has another field winding connected in *series* with the generator output, the same as a series generator. Compound generators are sometimes referred to as *series-shunt generators.*

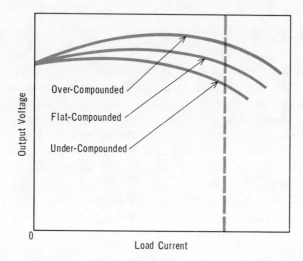

Whether a compound generator is flat-compounded, over-compounded, or under-compounded, the output voltage drops off sharply when the load current exceeds rated full load

compound generators (cont.)

The two windings of the compound generator are made so that their magnetic fields *aid* each other. Thus, when the load current increases, the current through the shunt field winding decreases, reducing the strength of its magnetic field. But the same increase in load current flows through the series field winding, increasing the strength of its magnetic field.

With the proper number of turns in the series winding, the increase in strength in its magnetic field will *compensate* for the decrease in strength of the magnetic field of the shunt winding. The overall strength of the combined magnetic field, therefore, remains almost unchanged, so the output voltage stays constant. Actually, the two field windings cannot be made so that their magnetic fields exactly compensate for one another. Some change in output voltage will take place as the generator current varies from no-load to full-load value. However, as shown in the graph, in practical compound generators, the output voltage at no load and full load is the same, and the change that takes place between no load and full load is less than about 5 percent. A generator with these characteristics is said to be *flat-compounded*.

For some applications, the series winding is made so that it over-compensates for the shunt winding. The generator output voltage then gradually increases with increasing load current over the normal operating range. Such a generator is *over-compounded*. Similarly, the series winding can be made so that it under-compensates for the shunt winding. The output voltage of this type of generator decreases gradually with increasing load current. This type of generator is *under-compounded*.

starting self-excited generators

At the instant any generator is started, both its output voltage and current are zero. You may wonder, therefore, how a self-excited generator can begin to develop an output voltage. With no voltage across the field winding or current through it, how does the winding produce the magnetic field that it must have if the generator is to operate? The answer lies in the *residual magnetism* of the pole pieces. Whenever magnetic materials have been magnetized, they *hold* a small *portion* of this magnetism even after the magnetizing influence is removed.

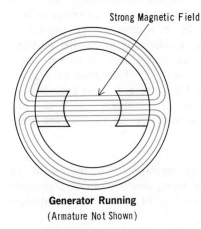

Generator Running
(Armature Not Shown)

The residual magnetism of the pole pieces makes it possible to start a self-excited generator even though no exciting current flows through the field windings at the instant the generator is started

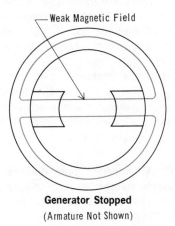

Generator Stopped
(Armature Not Shown)

The residual magnetism is caused by the fact that even when the magnetizing current is removed, the pole pieces remain slightly magnetized

Soft iron, of which the pole pieces are made, loses most of its magnetism whenever the exciting current through the field winding drops to zero, such as when the generator is turned off. It retains a small portion of its magnetism, though, and so maintains a *weak* magnetic field in the space between the pole pieces. So, when the generator is started again, the armature coils cut the flux lines of this weak magnetic field. This induces a small voltage in the armature coils, which gives the generator a weak output. The output then causes some exciting current to flow, thereby increasing the strength of the magnetic field, which increases the voltage induced in the armature coils. This action continues until the generator reaches its rated output. In some cases, it can take as long as 30 seconds from the time a self-excited generator is turned on until it reaches its rated output.

summary

☐ Electromagnets used to produce the magnetic field of a generator are called field coils. ☐ Field coils are wound around pole pieces. ☐ A simple generator has two field coils, and is called a two-pole generator. ☐ All of the field coils together are called the field winding. ☐ The current that excites the field winding of a d-c generator must be dc. ☐ In a separately excited generator, the excitation current is supplied by an external d-c voltage source. ☐ In a self-excited generator, the excitation current is supplied by the generator's own output.

☐ There are three types of self-excited generators: series, shunt, and compound. ☐ In a series generator, the field winding is connected in series with the generator output. ☐ A series generator has poor voltage regulation. ☐ In a shunt generator, the field winding is connected in parallel with the generator output. ☐ Shunt generators have better regulation and much smaller excitation current than series generators. ☐ If the load on a shunt generator is shorted, the output voltage will drop to zero. This provides the shunt generator with a self-protective feature. ☐ A compound generator has two field windings: one connected in series with the output, and the other in parallel with it.

☐ A compound generator has good voltage regulation, with the change in output voltage between no load and full load being less than about 5 percent. ☐ A self-excited generator is self-starting because of the residual magnetism of the pole pieces.

review questions

1. What is *excitation current*?
2. Why must the excitation current in a d-c generator be dc?
3. What is a *self-excited generator*? A *separately-excited generator*?
4. Why does a series generator have poor voltage regulation?
5. Why are shunt generators said to be self protective?
6. Why must heavy wire be used for the field windings of series generators?
7. What is a *compound generator*?
8. What is an *over-compounded generator*? An *under-compounded generator*?
9. When a self-excited generator is started, why does it take some time for it to reach its rated output?
10. In a compound generator, do the magnetic fields of the two windings aid or oppose each other?

the armature winding

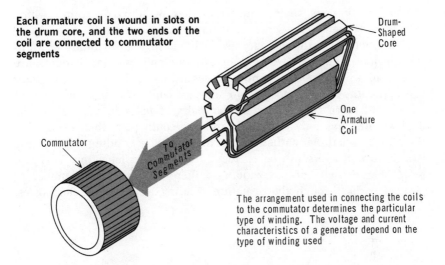

Each armature coil is wound in slots on the drum core, and the two ends of the coil are connected to commutator segments

Drum-Shaped Core

One Armature Coil

Commutator

To Commutator Segments

The arrangement used in connecting the coils to the commutator determines the particular type of winding. The voltage and current characteristics of a generator depend on the type of winding used

Just as the combined field coils make up the field winding, the combined armature coils are called the *armature winding*. The ends of each armature coil are connected to different segments on the commutator, where its emf is picked up by the brushes. The coils of all modern generator armatures are wound on an iron core that is shaped like a drum. The core provides a means for rotating the coils, and, at the same time, is a good low-reluctance path for the flux lines of the magnetic field set up by the field winding. The core has slots along its length, and the coils are wound in these slots. The two sides of each coil are positioned in different slots. A typical drum core with one three-turn armature coil in place is shown.

The ends of the armature coils can be connected to the commutator segments in many different ways. The arrangement used determines to a large extent the voltage and current characteristics of the generator. For practical purposes, all of the different arrangements can be divided into two main types: *lap windings* and *wave windings*. When lap or wave windings are combined, it is called a *frog-leg winding*, because of the shape that is produced.

In any armature winding, either lap or wave, an important point to remember is that each coil is wound on the core in such a way that the two sides of the coil are separated by the same distance that separates a north field pole from a south field pole. Therefore, whenever one side of a coil is at the middle of a north pole, the other side is at the middle of a south pole.

lap windings

Lap windings get their name from their winding diagrams, which represent the connections between the armature coils and the commutator segments. On these diagrams, each coil of a lap winding *overlaps* the previous coil. The two ends of any one coil in a lap winding are connected to *adjacent* commutator segments, and each commutator segment connects the ends of two adjacent coils. This has the effect of placing all those coils under similar pairs of poles in parallel. If the field winding has only one north and one south pole, this means that there are two parallel paths through the armature winding. If there are two north and two south poles, there are four parallel paths. This is a basic characteristic of lap windings: there are the same number of parallel paths through the armature winding as there are field poles.

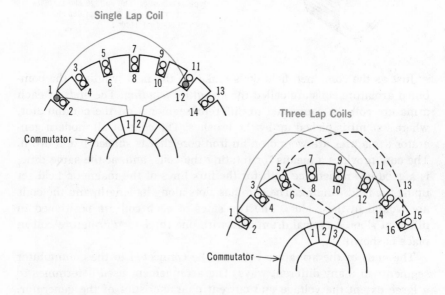

The voltages induced in the coils in each of the parallel paths are equal and have the same polarity, so no circulating current flows among the parallel paths. There is one set of brushes for each two parallel paths, and they are electrically connected (negative to negative and positive to positive) at the generator output. The output voltage is, therefore, equal to the voltage induced in any one of the parallel paths, but the current capacity is large, since the current divides among many paths inside of the generator. Lap windings, therefore, sacrifice voltage output for current capacity.

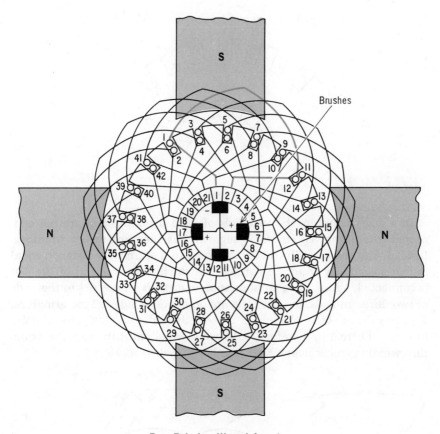

Four-Pole Lap-Wound Armature

lap windings (cont.)

In summary, lap windings divide the armature winding into as many parallel paths as there are field poles. The voltages induced in the coils in any one of these parallel paths add to produce the total voltage of that path. The total voltages induced in each path are equal and of the same polarity, and so therefore are the currents in each path. There is one set of brushes for each two paths, or, in other words, one brush for each pole, and the combined outputs of each set of brushes make up the generator output. Since the brushes are in parallel, the output voltage is the same as that between any one set of brushes. The output current, though, is the sum of the currents flowing through each set of brushes.

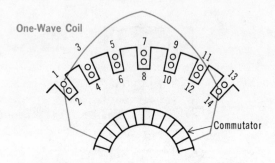

One-Wave Coil

Commutator

wave windings

In a *wave winding*, the two ends of each armature coil are not connected to adjacent commutator segments as they are in lap windings. Instead, one end of each coil is connected to a segment a distance equal to *two poles* away from the segment to which the other end of the coil is connected; again, each commutator segment is connected to the ends of two different coils, but the coils are on opposite sides of the armature. This has the effect of placing all those coils under similar pairs of poles in *series*. There are, therefore, only two parallel paths through the armature winding, regardless of the number of poles.

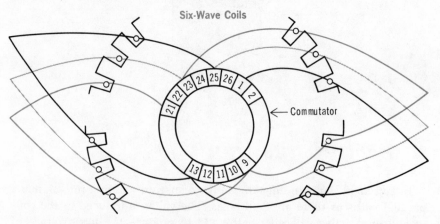

Six-Wave Coils

Commutator

The individual coil voltages add in each path, and since there are only two paths, there are more coils per path than there are in a comparable lap winding. The total voltage induced in each path, therefore, is relatively high. The current capacity of a wave winding, though, is lower than that of a lap winding because there are only two paths for current through the winding. You can see, then, that whereas a lap winding sacrifices output voltage for current-carrying capacity, a wave winding sacrifices current-carrying capacity to achieve high voltage.

wave windings (cont.)

For the same number and size of armature coils, a wave winding will produce a voltage equal to that produced by a lap winding times the number of pairs of poles. But the current capacity is decreased in the same proportion that the voltage is increased. For a simple two-pole generator, it makes no difference whether a lap or wave winding is used. There are two parallel paths through the winding in either case, so the output voltage and current capacity will be the same.

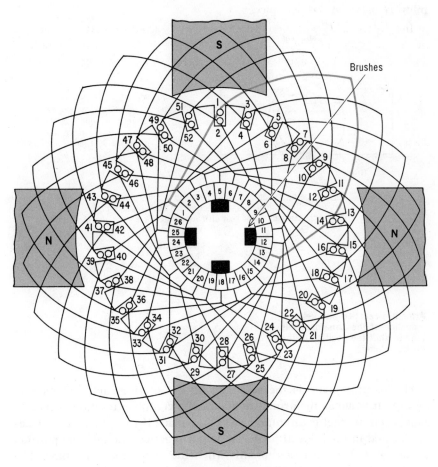

Four-Pole Wave-Wound Armature

the neutral plane

You will recall from the discussion on the basic commutator that whenever a brush makes contact with two commutator segments having a coil connected between them, the brush *short-circuits* the coil. If a voltage was being induced in the coil at this time, a large current would flow through the coil and probably burn it out. To prevent this, a coil must only be shorted by a brush, or *commutated,* when its induced voltage is zero. The points in its rotation where a coil has zero induced voltage lie along what is called the *neutral plane.* As shown for a two-pole generator, the neutral plane is perpendicular to the flux lines and midway between the pole pieces.

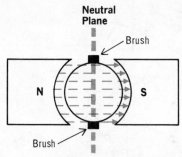

The neutral plane is theoretically where the armature coils cut no flux lines, and so have no voltage induced in them

During operation, the neutral plane tends to shift to a new position. Because of this, the theoretical neutral plane is called the mechanical or geometrical neutral plane

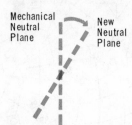

Armature reaction and self-induction of the armature coils tend to shift the position of the neutral plane

The neutral plane is the same for all coils, with each coil passing through it twice as the armature makes one complete rotation. Theoretically, then, perfect commutation will take place if the generator brushes are located in the neutral plane. In actual practice, though, the position of the neutral plane tends to shift when the generator is running. The brushes, therefore, either have to be moved to the new position of the neutral plane, or something must be done to prevent the plane from shifting. The two causes of this shifting of the neutral plane are *armature reaction* and *self-induction* of the armature coils.

armature reaction

When a generator supplies current to a load, the same current that flows through the load also flows through the armature winding. This causes a *magnetic field* to be built up around the conductors of the *armature winding*, since current through any conductor will produce a magnetic field. The magnetic fields around the individual conductors of the armature winding combine to produce an overall magnetic field. There are thus *two* magnetic fields in the space between the generator pole pieces. One is the field caused by the current through the armature, and the other is the main magnetic field produced by the field winding.

It is characteristic of magnetic fields that their flux lines cannot cross; instead, they *combine* to produce a new, total magnetic field. The total field of the two individual fields between the generator pole pieces has a direction as shown. This is the actual field cut by the armature coils as the armature rotates. Zero voltage is still induced in each coil when it cuts no lines of flux, but the two points at which this occurs are no longer in the same place as they were when only the magnetic field of the field winding was considered. The two points have both been *shifted* in the direction of armature rotation. This means, therefore, that the neutral plane has been shifted in the direction of armature rotation.

The neutral plane shift depends on the strength of the magnetic field set up around the armature winding by the load current. The larger the load current, the more the neutral plane shifts. The direction of shift though, is always the same as the direction of rotation. You can see, then, that if the load is constant, the brushes can be positioned at the new location of the neutral plane and left there. But if the load on the generator changes frequently, the brushes must constantly be changed to the new position of the neutral plane if good commutation is to take place. This is obviously a troublesome procedure.

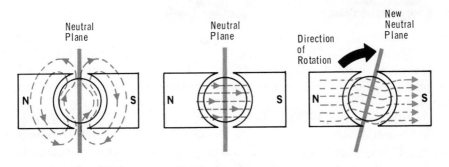

Magnetic field produced by current through armature winding

Magnetic field produced by field winding

Combined magnetic field

self-induction of armature coils

You have seen how the neutral plane is shifted in the direction of rotation by the effect of armature reaction. If you know the exact amount of this shift, and were to set the generator brushes accordingly, you would actually still not get perfect commutation. This is because of *self-induction* of the armature coils.

When the current through a coil tends to drop to zero at the point where the coil is cutting no flux lines, the magnetic field around the coil collapses. You should recall from Volume 3 that this causes a self-induced voltage, which has a polarity that keeps the current flowing, instead of allowing it to drop instantly to zero. This self-induced voltage, then, appears between the commutator segments when the coils are in what is supposedly the neutral plane. Although the self-induced voltage is small, it can cause a large current because of the low resistance of the commutator segments, the brushes, and the coil. This means that the voltage in a coil is not zero until sometime after the coil has passed the point in its rotation where it is cutting no flux lines.

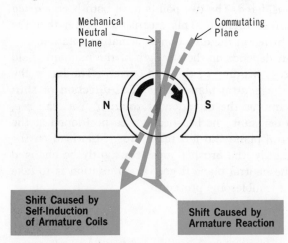

Mechanical Neutral Plane

Commutating Plane

N   S

In addition to the shift of the neutral plane caused by armature reaction, there is a further shift caused by the self-induction of the armature coils. Both shifts are in the direction of rotation

Shift Caused by Self-Induction of Armature Coils

Shift Caused by Armature Reaction

Effectively, then, the self-induced voltage has *further shifted* the neutral plane in the direction of rotation. This new position of the neutral plane is often called the *electrical neutral plane*, or the *commutating plane*.

If the generator brushes are located in this plane, good commutation will result. Like armature reaction, the shift in the neutral plane caused by self-induction of the armature coils is proportional to the load current. Therefore, as was mentioned before, good commutation can only be obtained if the load current is constant, or if the position of the brushes is changed every time the load current charges.

Two-Pole Generator With Interpoles

Direction of Rotation

Interpoles

Generator
Output

Interpoles are connected in
series with the armature
winding so that their
magnetic fields oppose the
field of the armature winding

N   DC   S

Interpoles completely eliminate the shift of the neutral
plane due to self-induction
of the armature coils, and
partly eliminate the shift
due to armature reaction

Interpoles are small windings located at
the mechanical neutral plane

interpoles

When a generator is to supply a variable ʌad current, some provision
must be made to keep the neutral plane from shifting as the load current changes. Without such a provision, constant changing of the position of the brushes would be required. One way of keeping the actual
neutral plane close to the mechanical neutral plane despite changes in
load is by the use of *interpoles*. As shown, interpoles are small windings located at the mechanical neutral plane. The windings are wound
around pole pieces that are part of the generator housing. The interpole
windings are connected in series with the armature winding, so the load
current causes a magnetic field to be set up around each interpole.

The directions of these magnetic fields are such that they *cancel* the
magnetic field around the armature coils in the vicinity of the interpoles. With no magnetic field to collapse, therefore, there is no self-
induction of the armature coils when they reach the neutral plane. So,
no shift of the neutral plane occurs due to self-induction of the armature
coils. To do their job, interpoles must have the correct polarity, which is
opposite to that of the emf of self-induction. If you use the left-hand
rule, you will see that the interpole polarity must be the same as the
next field pole in the direction of rotation.

Interpoles are self-regulating. When the load current increases, the
neutral plane tends to shift in the direction of rotation. But, at the same
time, the field of the interpoles increases in strength, and so opposes
the shift.

compensating windings

Interpoles cannot eliminate armature reaction because they are located only at the neutral plane while armature reaction takes place all around the armature. But, if interpoles were placed all around the armature, armature reaction could be eliminated. In effect, this is what is done by *compensating windings,* which are small windings set in the main pole pieces. The compensating windings are in *series* with each other and with the armature winding.

Compensating windings are small series windings set in the main pole pieces

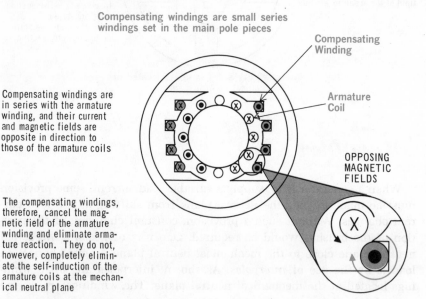

Compensating windings are in series with the armature winding, and their current and magnetic fields are opposite in direction to those of the armature coils

The compensating windings, therefore, cancel the magnetic field of the armature winding and eliminate armature reaction. They do not, however, completely eliminate the self-induction of the armature coils at the mechanical neutral plane

Compensating Winding

Armature Coil

OPPOSING MAGNETIC FIELDS

As shown, the current in the compensating windings flows in the *opposite* direction of the current in the armature coils that face them. Since the currents are opposite, the direction of the magnetic fields of the compensating windings and the armature coils are also opposite. This means that the field of the compensating windings cancels the field of the armature coils. By canceling the magnetic field of the armature coils, the compensating windings eliminate armature reaction, but it does not do away completely with the self-induction of the armature coils.

You can see that both compensating windings and interpoles eliminate most of the shift in the neutral plane that would otherwise be caused by load changes. Some variable load generators use compensating windings, while others use interpoles. On very large generators, or those with wide load variations, compensating windings and interpoles are often used together.

regulating generator voltage

The voltage produced by any d-c generator depends on three factors: (1) the number of conductor loops in the armature that are in series, (2) the speed at which the armature rotates, and (3) the strength of the magnetic field. For a generator to provide a constant voltage output under varying load, at least one of these three factors must be varied to compensate for the voltage changes that the load changes would otherwise cause. During normal operation, neither the number of conductors in the armature, nor their arrangement can be changed. It is also impractical to change the speed at which the armature rotates. The strength of the magnetic field, though, can be changed relatively easily by varying the current through the field winding, and as a result, this is the method used mostly to regulate the output voltage of a generator.

Voltage Regulators Are Often Used With Shunt Generators

When used with shunt generators, voltage regulators function as variable resistors in series with the field winding. They automatically adjust the field current to compensate for changes in the generator output voltage

Voltage Regulator

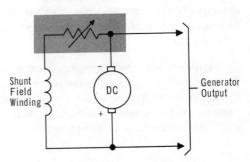

Shunt Field Winding

DC

Generator Output

You have learned how compound generators provide a relatively constant voltage because their field current automatically adjusts to compensate for changes in load current. By using auxiliary devices or circuits called *voltage regulators,* generators can be made to have output voltages even more stable than those of compound generators. Voltage regulators vary widely in type and design; but they all perform two basic functions: they *sense* the generator output voltage, and they *vary* the current through the field winding in response to the output voltage. Thus, if the regulator senses that the voltage has dropped, it increases the field current to bring the voltage back to normal. Similarly, if the output voltage rises, the regulator decreases the field current. Normally, voltage regulators control the field current either by varying a *resistance* in series with the field, or one in parallel with the field.

In many cases, the regulating resistor is adjusted manually to obtain the right meter reading. For large generators that supply very high currents, special resistance devices are used. One such device is the *carbon pile regulator.*

summary

☐ In a lap winding, the armature winding is divided into as many parallel paths as there are field poles. One set of brushes is used for each two paths. ☐ Lap windings sacrifice voltage output for current capacity. ☐ In a wave winding, all armature coils under similar pairs of poles are in series. There are, therefore, only two parallel paths through the armature. ☐ Wave windings sacrifice current-carrying capacity for high voltage.

☐ The neutral plane is the point in the rotation of an armature where its induced voltage is zero. ☐ When a generator is running, the neutral plane tends to shift as a result of armature reaction and self-induction of the armature coils. ☐ Armature reaction is caused by the magnetic field built up around the armature winding by the load current. ☐ Armature reaction shifts the neutral plane in the direction of armature rotation. ☐ Self-induction of the armature coils prevents the coil voltage from instantly dropping to zero when the coil is cutting no flux lines. ☐ The neutral plane is shifted further in the direction of rotation by the self-induction of the armature coils. ☐ The new position of the neutral plane produced by armature reaction and self-induction of the armature coils is called the electrical neutral plane. ☐ Good commutation results when the generator brushes are located at the electrical neutral plane.

☐ Interpoles are small windings located at the mechanical neutral plane. They are used to compensate for self-induction of the armature coils. ☐ Compensating windings are small windings set in the main pole pieces. They compensate for armature reaction. ☐ Voltage regulators are used to maintain a stable output voltage from a generator.

review questions

1. What are the basic characteristics of a lap winding?
2. In general, does a lap or wave winding have a greater current capacity?
3. What is the *mechanical neutral plane*?
4. What is *armature reaction*?
5. Can armature reaction be eliminated by holding the load current constant?
6. What is the *electrical neutral plane*?
7. How does self-induction of the armature coils affect the electrical neutral plane?
8. What are interpoles used for?
9. What are *compensating windings*?
10. If the output voltage of a generator tends to increase, what should be done to the current through the field winding to keep the voltage constant?

construction

The fundamental principles of operation of d-c generators have been described. You know the basic parts of a generator, the function of each of these parts, and the relationship each part has to the overall operation of the generator. Essentially, what you have learned is the *electrical operation* of a d-c generator. The *physical construction* has been covered only briefly. Very often, you will find that it is important for you not only to know how a generator works electrically, but to be able to recogize its various parts and be familiar with their physical construction.

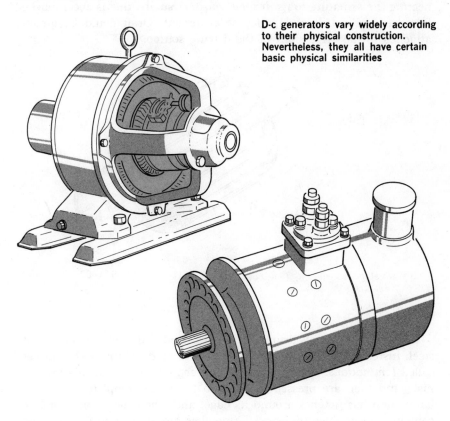

D-c generators vary widely according to their physical construction. Nevertheless, they all have certain basic physical similarities

It is beyond the scope of this volume to describe the construction details of all the many types of d-c generators now in use. However, there are basic physical similarities between practically all generators. Because of this, if you know how a typical generator is made, you will have a good idea of the physical construction of most others. The materials and methods used in the construction of a typical d-c generator, therefore, are described on the following pages.

the armature

The armature, or armature assembly as it is sometimes called, consists of all those generator parts that *rotate*. These parts are the armature *shaft,* the armature *core*, the armature *winding*, and the *commutator*. As shown, the core and the commutator are mounted on the shaft. The winding is wound around the core, in slots, and the ends of the individual coils that make up the winding are connected to the commutator segments. Although not shown, there is one other part that must be mounted on the armature shaft. This is the device or means for connecting the armature to its *driving source*. Usually, this is accomplished by a gear or a belt and pulley arrangement. Or it could be directly attached to the drive shaft of the driving source.

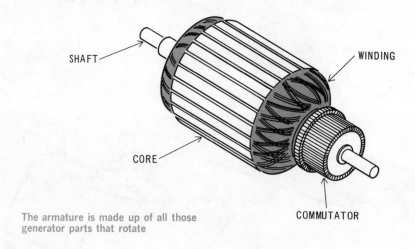

SHAFT

WINDING

CORE

COMMUTATOR

The armature is made up of all those generator parts that rotate

The armature core is drum-shaped, or cylindrical, and is made of soft steel. Instead of being one piece, the core is made of many thin pieces, called *laminations*. The laminations are coated with an insulating varnish, and then are pressed together to form the complete core. Each lamination has notches around its edge, and when the laminations are combined to produce the core, the notches are aligned so that the core has slots along its perimeter. The reason the core is laminated is to reduce losses due to *eddy currents*, which you remember (Volume 3) are circulating currents that are induced in a conducting material when it cuts through magnetic flux lines. The laminations have the effect of greatly reducing the area in which the eddy currents can flow; and this means that the resistance of the material to eddy current flow is greatly increased.

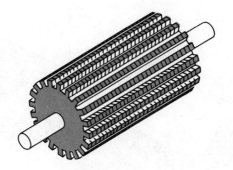

One Core Lamination

Laminated Core Mounted
on Armature Shaft

The armature core is laminated to reduce eddy current losses. It is made
of silicon steel to reduce hysteresis losses

the armature (cont.)

To reduce the *hysteresis loss* of the core, which you will recall (Volume 3) occurs because the reversals of the magnetization of the core material actually *lag* the current reversals, practically all generators have cores made of soft silicon steel. This material has an inherently low hysteresis loss.

The generator shaft is a rod made of hard steel, finished with a highly polished bearing surface. The method of mounting the core and the commutator on the shaft varies widely from generator to generator.

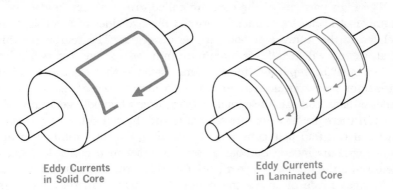

Eddy Currents
in Solid Core

Eddy Currents
in Laminated Core

By laminating the core, the eddy currents are divided into many small
currents, greatly decreasing the eddy current losses

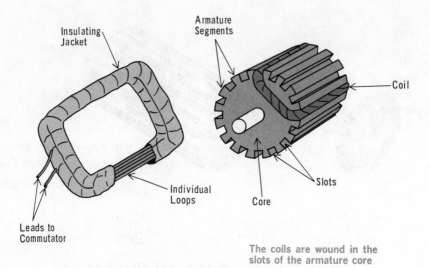

Each coil consists of one or more loops wrapped together in a common insulating jacket

The coils are wound in the slots of the armature core

the armature winding

Each of the coils that make up the armature winding are wound around the armature core, with the sides of the coils set into the slots in the core. In many armatures, the coils are first formed into their final shape, and then placed on the core. This is called *form winding*. All of the loops in a coil are *wrapped together* in a common insulating jacket, and each coil has only *two leads* for connecting to the commutator.

The high portions of the core are called *armature segments,* and the number of armature segments between the two sides of a coil is directly related to the number of poles in the generator. The reason for this is that, as you will recall, for maximum induced voltage, the two sides of a coil must be separated by the same distance that separates adjacent generator poles. Thus, if there are 24 armature segments and the two sides of each coil are 12 segments apart, it is a two-pole generator. Similarly, if there are 24 armature segments and the coil sides are 6 segments apart, it is a four-pole generator. By dividing the total number of armature segments by the number of segments between coil sides, you can determine the number of segments for which the armature was wound.

Wedges made of insulating material are placed in the core slots to hold the coils in place. On some generators, steel bands are also placed around the armature to prevent the coils from being thrown out by centrifugal force.

the commutator

The commutator consists of individual segments made of hand-drawn copper and shaped as shown. The individual segments are assembled in cylindrical form, and are held together by a *clamping flange*. The segments are placed in the wedge-shaped space between the two halves of the clamping flange, and the flange bolts are then tightened, holding the segments rigidly in place. The segments are *insulated* from each other with thin sheets of *mica*. They are also insulated from the clamping flange with rings of mica.

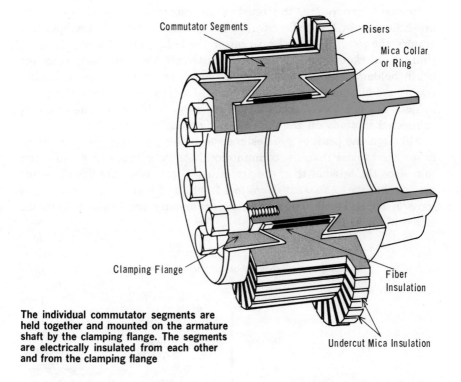

The individual commutator segments are held together and mounted on the armature shaft by the clamping flange. The segments are electrically insulated from each other and from the clamping flange

The leads from the armature coils are connected to the raised portions of the commutator segments, called *risers*. Some commutator segments have no risers. In these cases, the leads from the armature coils are connected to slits in the end of the segments.

The surface of the commutator is cut and ground to a very smooth cylindrical finish. This insures a minimum of friction between the commutator surface and the brushes. In addition, the mica insulation is *undercut* slightly below the surface of the commutator segments so that it does not interfere with the brushes.

the brushes

The brushes transfer the generator output from the commutator to an external circuit. They are usually small blocks of a *carbon* and *graphite* compound. *No lubrication* should be used between the brushes and the commutator, since the graphite in the brushes provides self-lubrication. The brushes are set in holders and held against the commutators by springs. In many generators, the spring pressure can be adjusted. If the pressure is set too high, the brushes will wear out quickly. And if too low a pressure is used, poor electrical contact between the brushes and the commutator results.

In many generators, the brushes are electrically connected to the brush holders by braided copper wires called *pigtails;* but in simple generators, the close fit of the brush inside the holder provides the electrical connection. Connections to an external circuit are then made from the brush holders. The brush holders, although mounted on the generator frame, are electrically insulated from it. In many generators, the brush holders are not easily accessible. The brush holders are then usually connected to *studs* on the outside of the generator housing.

Although the brushes are designed to be long lasting, they are made to wear out faster than the commutator, because it is cheaper and easier to replace the brushes than the armature. The brushes are usually made long so that they can wear down to a fraction of their length before they have to be replaced. The spring keeps moving the brush toward the commutator as it wears.

Brushes Are Usually Made of Carbon and Graphite

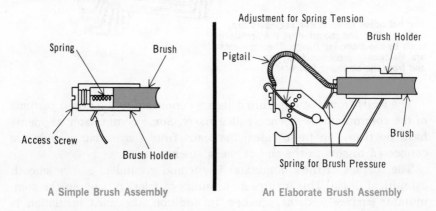

A Simple Brush Assembly   An Elaborate Brush Assembly

Brushes are held in holders, and are pressed against the commutator by springs. Good generators have a tension adjustment to allow proper brush contact with minimum wear

the field winding

The field winding of a generator consists of the individual field coils wound around their cores, or pole pieces. The number of field coils depends on how many poles the generator has. In a two-pole generator, there are two field coils; in a four-pole generator, four coils; and so forth. The field coils are mounted on the inside circumference of the generator housing with large countersunk screws that pass through the housing and into the pole pieces.

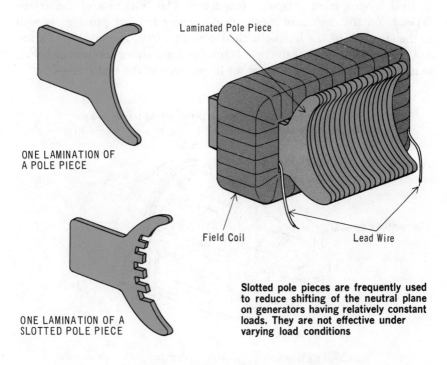

Laminated Pole Piece

ONE LAMINATION OF A POLE PIECE

Field Coil

Lead Wire

ONE LAMINATION OF A SLOTTED POLE PIECE

Slotted pole pieces are frequently used to reduce shifting of the neutral plane on generators having relatively constant loads. They are not effective under varying load conditions

The pole pieces are usually made of sheets of steel *laminated* together. This decreases losses due to eddy currents. As shown, the pole pieces are shaped to fit the curvature of the armature. The purpose of this is to keep the *air gap* between the pole pieces and the armature as *small* as possible, since air offers a relatively high reluctance to magnetic flux lines.

The field coils are wound around the pole pieces. *Shunt windings* consist of *many turns* of relatively *small-diameter* insulated copper wire. *Series windings*, on the other hand, consist of a *few turns* of *large-diameter* copper wire, also insulated. The wire used in series windings must be large enough to carry the entire load current without overheating.

the housing and mounting

The generator housing provides *mechanical support* for the parts that make up the generator. On many generators, it also provides protection against outside disturbances such as dust, dirt, and moisture. Most generator housings consist of three parts: a *field frame*, and two *end frames*. The field frame supports the field coils, as well as the interpoles, if they are used. It also serves as part of the magnetic circuit of the field winding. Because of its magnetic function, the field frame is made of iron or steel having good magnetic properties. The thickness of the frame depends on the degree of mechanical support it must provide, as well as the strength of the magnetic field it must carry. The end frames are mounted at either end of the field frame, and are either screwed or bolted to it. The armature bearings are set in recesses in the end frames.

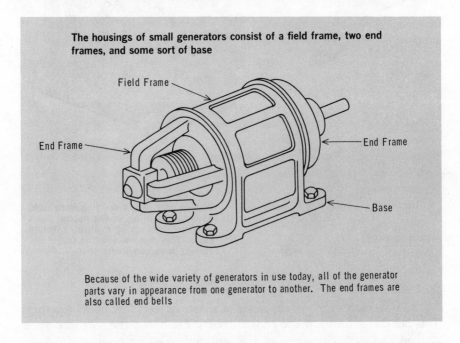

The housings of small generators consist of a field frame, two end frames, and some sort of base

Field Frame

End Frame

End Frame

Base

Because of the wide variety of generators in use today, all of the generator parts vary in appearance from one generator to another. The end frames are also called end bells

There are many methods used for mounting generators, with the method used in any particular case depending on factors such as the size and use of the generator, and the type of source that is driving it. Probably the most common type of mounting is the simple base. This consists of legs or other supports either attached to or part of the field frame, and on which the generator sits. Another common mounting method consists of a flange or plate at the drive end of the generator. The plate has holes in it, and can be bolted to another plate or a panel.

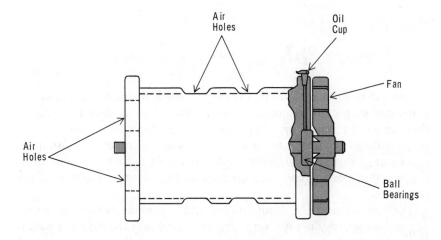

Proper lubrication and cooling are required if a
generator is to give long and efficient service

other construction features

Two other important construction features of d-c generators are the
bearings and the *cooling methods* used. Practically all smaller type generators use ball bearings to provide smooth, high-speed armature rotation
with a minimum of friction. The bearings are force-fitted on the ends of
the armature shaft, and are set in recesses in the end frames. Thus, when
the end frames are screwed or bolted to the field frame, the armature
is supported by the end frames. The bearings on some generators are
permanently lubricated, and sealed during manufacture. No further
lubrication of these bearings during use is required, or possible. On
generators where the bearings are not sealed, some means is provided
for periodic lubrication. Usually, this is in the form of a grease or oil
cup in the end frames.

When a generator operates at full capacity, it develops considerable
heat. The most common method of dissipating this heat is by means of
air holes and a *fan.* The air holes are openings in the end frames and
in the field frame near the field windings. On larger generators, there
are also air holes through the armature. The fan is mounted on one end
of the armature shaft. When the armature rotates, the fan forces air
through the air holes. The air thus picks up heat from inside the generator housing, and carries it through the air holes to the outside of the
housing. Heavy-load generators are often also mounted on a large metal
area, referred to as a *heat sink,* which helps conduct the heat away.

regulating
a variable-speed generator

You will recall that regulation is the process of maintaining a *constant* generator output. It is normally accomplished by a device or circuit that senses the generator output, and controls the current through the field winding to compensate for any changes in the output. The two main causes of change, or instability, in a generator's output are changes in the *resistance* of the *load* and changes in the *speed of rotation* of the generator.

The output voltage of shunt and compound generators that are driven at constant speeds does not vary greatly if the load variations are within the design range of the generator. As a result, regulation is only provided for these generators when an extremely stable output is desired, or when the load variations are very great.

Variable-speed generators, on the other hand, usually require regulation. You can understand why by considering the generator used in an automobile. The generator is turned by the automobile engine, so its speed of rotation is very different when the engine is idling than it is when the automobile is traveling at high speed. And yet, despite this wide variation in its speed of rotation, the generator must supply a constant 6 or 12 volts to the electrical system of the automobile. If this voltage should vary, the lights, the horn, in fact the entire electrical system, would be affected. The only way such a generator can supply a stable 6 or 12 volts is by the use of a regulating device. And not only must the regulating device keep the output voltage constant, it must also limit the *output current* of the generator to its maximum rated value to prevent the generator from burning out. Thus, both voltage and current regulation are normally required for a variable-speed generator.

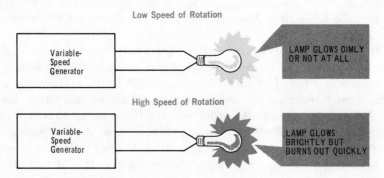

Low Speed of Rotation

Variable-Speed Generator

LAMP GLOWS DIMLY OR NOT AT ALL

High Speed of Rotation

Variable-Speed Generator

LAMP GLOWS BRIGHTLY BUT BURNS OUT QUICKLY

If variable-speed generators did not have their outputs regulated, the loads they supply could not work properly

voltage regulation

A typical circuit used for regulating the generator output voltage is shown. One side of the shunt field winding is connected *directly* to the negative output of the generator. The other side of the field winding is connected to the positive side of the generator output either through resistor R and coil L_2, or through contacts C, which are controlled by the magnetic field of L_1. Thus, the field winding is either directly across the generator output (C closed), or it has R connected in series with it (C open).

The contacts are held closed by a spring so that when the generator is first turned on, the contacts are closed, and the field winding is directly across the generator output. As the generator builds up speed, its output voltage increases, and so also does the current through L_1, which is connected directly across the generator output. When the output voltage reaches a certain point, the magnetic field of L_1 is strong enough to overcome the spring holding C closed, and so C opens.

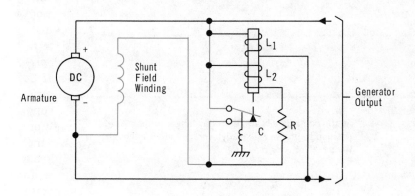

The voltage regulator operates by contacts intermittently inserting a resistance in series with the field winding

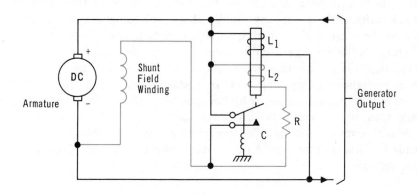

voltage regulation (cont.)

The field current now flows through R and L_2. With the added resistance in the field circuit, the field strength decreases, and the rise in the generator output voltage is checked. The current through L_2 causes a magnetic field around L_2, and this field opposes that around L_1, since the two coils are oppositely wound. This partially neutralizes the magnetic attraction of L_1 on C, and the spring again closes C. As a result, the field winding is again directly across the generator output, so the field current increases, increasing the output voltage, which in turn causes C to open due to the increased magnetic pull of L_1.

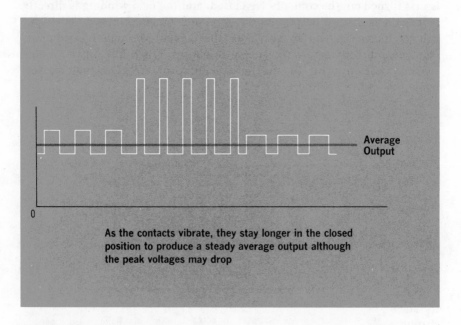

As the contacts vibrate, they stay longer in the closed position to produce a steady average output although the peak voltages may drop

This cycle occurs very rapidly, many times a second, causing the contacts to vibrate open and closed. The output voltage of the generator thus varies slightly but very rapidly above and below a value determined by the tension of the spring holding C closed. The actual d-c output voltage is the average value between the high and low points. This average depends on whether the contacts stay longer in one position than in the other as they vibrate. If they stay closed longer than they stay open, the average voltage is higher, and vice versa. When the peak voltage goes up, the contacts stay longer in the open position to keep the average output constant. The spring is adjustable, and its setting controls the vibrating action of the contacts and the average generator output voltage.

current regulation

The current regulator, like the voltage regulator, operates by
intermittently inserting a resistance in series with the field winding

In the current regulator, the
insertion of the resistance
is controlled by the load
current, whereas in the voltage regulator it is controlled
by the output voltage

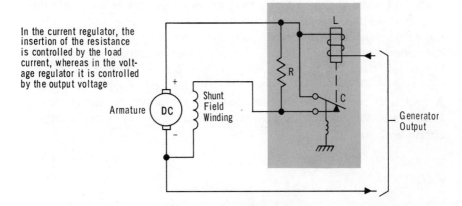

The purpose of regulating the output current of a generator is to
prevent the current from exceeding the maximum value that the generator can safely deliver. A commonly used method of current regulation is shown. Essentially, it is very similar to the method for voltage
regulation. Depending on whether contacts C are open or closed, the
field winding is either directly across the generator output, or it has
resistance R in series with it. The opening and closing of C is controlled
by coil L, which is in series with the generator output, and so carries the
full load current.

Contacts C are normally held closed by a spring. So, when the generator starts, the field winding is directly across the generator output. The
output voltage, therefore, builds up, and the load current, which flows
through L, also increases. When the current increases to the point where
the magnetic attraction of L overcomes the tension on the spring that
holds C closed, the contacts open. This inserts resistance R in series
with the field winding, and causes the field current, and therefore the
output voltage, to decrease.

As a result, the load current also decreases. The decrease in current
then lessens the magnetic pull of L, and the spring closes C again. This
puts the field winding directly across the generator output, and allows
the current to again increase until the magnetic pull of L is sufficient
to overcome the spring and open C. As in the voltage regulator, this cycle
is continually repeated, and the current varies slightly above and below
the average value determined by the spring tension holding C closed.

reverse-current cutout relay

Often a variable-speed d-c generator is used in combination with a *storage battery* to supply power to a load. When the generator's speed, and therefore its output voltage, is low, the battery supplies power to the load. And when the generator comes up to speed and reaches its rated output, it supplies the power to the load, and at the same time *recharges* the battery. In this arrangement, though, some method must be used to disconnect the generator from the battery whenever the generator voltage is less than the battery voltage. Otherwise, the battery would discharge through the generator armature winding and possibly burn it out. A frequently used method for automatically disconnecting the generator from the battery makes use of a *reverse-current cutout relay*. A typical circuit is shown.

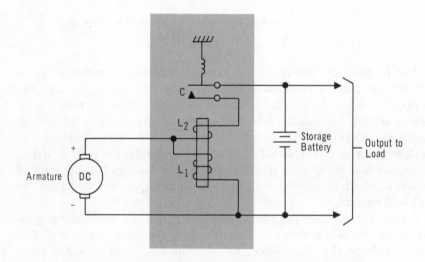

The reverse-current cutout relay connects the generator output to the battery and the load when the generator voltage is greater than the battery voltage. It then disconnects the generator from the battery and the load when the generator voltage drops below that of the battery

The reverse-current cutout relay consists of coils L_1 and L_2, both wound on the same core, and contacts C, which are normally held open by a spring. L_1 is called the voltage winding, and is connected across the generator output. L_2 is called the current winding, and is in series with the generator output.

reverse-current cutout relay (cont.)

The spring holding C open is adjusted so that when the generator voltage is less than the battery voltage, the contacts are open. The generator is therefore disconnected from both the battery and the load, and the battery supplies the output power. At all times, though, the generator output voltage is across L_1, causing current through the coil, and creating a magnetic field. When the generator output voltage rises above the battery voltage, the magnetic pull of L_1 overcomes the spring tension and closes C. This connects the generator to the load, and at the same time allows charging current to flow from the generator to the battery. The generator current flows through L_2, creating a magnetic field which aids that of L_1, and thus keeps the contacts closed tightly.

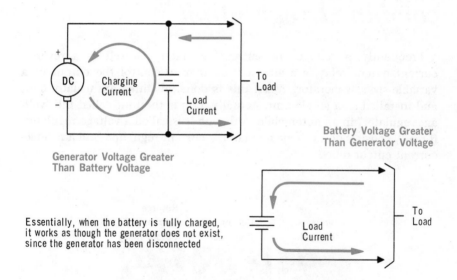

Generator Voltage Greater Than Battery Voltage

Battery Voltage Greater Than Generator Voltage

Essentially, when the battery is fully charged, it works as though the generator does not exist, since the generator has been disconnected

When the generator voltage is high enough to keep L_1 energized, but its voltage drops below that of the battery, the battery begins to discharge through L_2 and the generator. With the reversal of current through L_2, the magnetic field around it now opposes the magnetic field of L_1. This causes a decrease in the magnetic attraction on C, and as a result, the contacts open, disconnecting the generator from the battery and the load. You should note that the contacts of the reverse-current cutout relay do not vibrate continuously as do the contacts of the voltage and current regulators. They open or close only when the generator voltage either rises above or drops below the battery voltage.

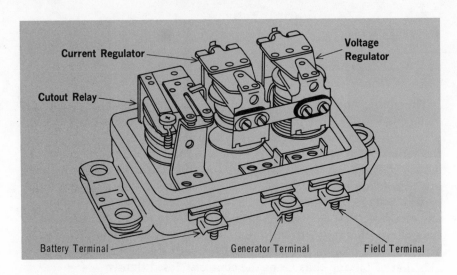

combined regulation

Frequently, a voltage and current regulator, as well as a reverse-current cutout relay, are all used together to control the output of a variable-speed generator. When this is done, all three are usually built and installed as a single unit. Actually, this is the unit called the "voltage regulator" in an automobile. Although it is called a voltage regulator, it really consists of a voltage regulator, a current regulator, and a reverse-current cutout relay.

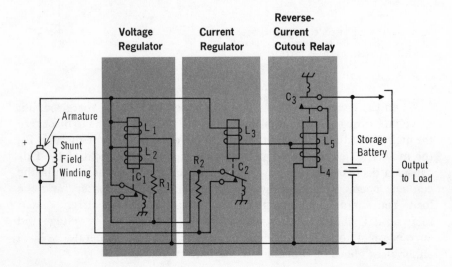

summary

☐ The armature of a d-c generator consists of all parts that rotate. These are: the armature shaft, the armature core, the armature winding, and the commutator. ☐ The armature shaft is a hard steel rod. ☐ The armature core is made of soft steel laminations insulated from each other. The core is laminated to reduce eddy current losses. ☐ The coils of the armature winding are wound around the core. ☐ The commutator is made of individual copper segments insulated from each other with thin sheets of mica. ☐ Leads from the armature coils are connected to the commutator segments.

☐ Generator brushes are usually small blocks of a carbon and graphite compound. The brushes are mounted in brush holders, which are electrically insulated from the generator frame. ☐ The individual coils of the field winding are wound around the generator pole pieces. ☐ Most generator housings consist of an iron or steel field frame and two end frames. ☐ The armature bearings are set in recesses in the end frames.

☐ Variable-speed generators normally require both voltage and current regulation. The voltage regulation maintains the output voltage essentially constant, while the current regulation prevents the output current from exceeding the maximum value that the generator can safely deliver. ☐ Reverse-current cutout-relay circuits are employed when a d-c generator is used in combination with a battery to supply power to a load. The circuit disconnects the generator from the battery whenever the generator voltage is less than the battery voltage.

review questions

1. Why is the armature core of a generator laminated?
2. Why is soft silicon steel generally used for the armature core of a generator?
3. What is *form winding*?
4. Must the commutator and brushes of a generator be lubricated? Why?
5. Why are pole pieces shaped to fit the curvature of the armature?
6. Physically, what is the difference between shunt and series field windings?
7. Could a plastic field frame be used for a generator? Why?
8. Why do variable-speed generators usually require both voltage and current regulation?
9. What is the purpose of a reverse-current cutout relay?
10. What are the two main causes of instability in a generator's output voltage?

a-c generators (alternators)

Although d-c generators are used extensively for certain applications, they have *inherent limitations* that make them unsatisfactory for many other uses. Some of these limitations are caused by the electrical and physical construction features of the d-c generators themselves, while others are due to the basic nature and properties of d-c electricity. Most of the limitations caused by the generators themselves arise from difficulties in constructing commutators that can carry large outputs reliably and efficiently. A-c generators, as you will learn, do not have commutators, and so in this respect are superior to d-c generators.

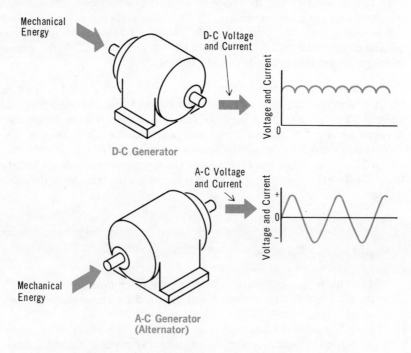

Both a-c and d-c generators convert mechanical energy into electrical energy. However, d-c generators convert mechanical energy into d-c voltages and currents, while a-c generators convert the mechanical energy into a-c voltages and currents

The theory of operation and construction characteristics of a-c generators are described on the following pages. You will find that there are many *basic similarities* between a-c and d-c generators. However, there are also many *significant differences,* as well as some electrical concepts that are entirely new to you. A-c generators are also called *alternators,* since they produce alternating current.

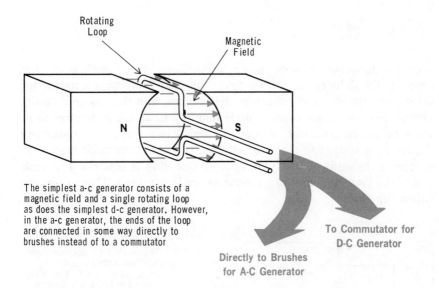

The simplest a-c generator consists of a magnetic field and a single rotating loop as does the simplest d-c generator. However, in the a-c generator, the ends of the loop are connected in some way directly to brushes instead of to a commutator

To Commutator for
D-C Generator

Directly to Brushes
for A-C Generator

the basic a-c generator

You will recall that the simplest d-c generator consists of a single loop of wire rotating in a magnetic field, plus a commutator and brushes. As the loop rotates, an a-c voltage is generated between its two ends. The a-c voltage is then converted to dc by the action of the commutator and brushes. The commutator accomplishes the ac to dc conversion by effectively *switching* the brushes from one end of the rotating loop to the other each time the voltage induced in the loop reverses polarity. This switching is done in such a way that *one brush* is always in contact with the end of the loop that is *positive,* while the *other brush* always contacts the end of the loop that is *negative.* The voltage between the brushes, which is the generator output voltage, is therefore dc.

If the commutator was eliminated, and each brush was permanently in contact with one end of the rotating loop, the voltage between the brushes would be exactly the same as the voltage existing between the ends of the loop. And as you know, this is an a-c voltage. Thus, by eliminating the commutator and in some way permanently connecting the brushes to opposite ends of the loop, the basic d-c generator can be converted to a simple a-c generator.

Of course, a direct connection of the ends of the loop cannot be made to the brushes because the ends must be free to rotate with the loop. If they were not free to rotate, they would become twisted as the loop turned and would break. So, in some way, the brushes must be permanently connected to their loop ends without interfering with their turning. This is covered next.

slip rings

The commutator in a d-c generator performs two functions: (1) it converts the induced a-c voltage to dc, and (2) it provides a means for connecting the induced voltage to the brushes, and thus to an external circuit. No conversion of ac to dc is required in an a-c generator, so in place of the commutator, all that is needed is a means of connecting the induced voltage to the brushes. This is done by *metallic rings* connected to the ends of the rotating loop. One ring is connected to each end of the loop, and both rings rotate as the loop rotates. These rings are called *slip rings*.

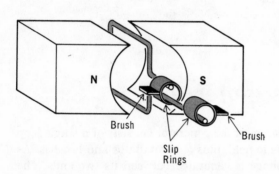

The slip rings are permanently connected to the ends of the loop. The brushes are stationary, and maintain contact with the slip rings as they rotate. The voltage induced in the loop is thus transferred to the brushes, and from there to an external circuit

Loop and Slip Rings Rotate While Brushes Remain Stationary

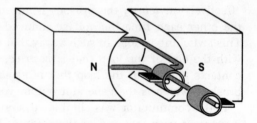

Each slip ring is *permanently* connected to its respective end of the rotating loop, so the voltage induced in the loop appears between the rings. The brushes rest against the slip rings and make electrical contact with them. As the loop rotates, the slip rings slide along the brushes, always maintaining electrical contact with them. Thus, each brush is always in contact with its slip ring, which in turn is permanently connected to one end of the loop. The result is that the a-c voltage induced in the loop appears between the brushes, and can then be applied to an external circuit.

generating a sine-wave output

You can see from the preceding pages that the output of the simple, one-loop a-c generator is identical to the voltage induced in the rotating loop. This voltage is equal to the *sum* of the voltages induced in the *two sides* of the loop as they cut the magnetic flux lines. When *no* flux lines are being cut, the voltage is *zero;* and when the *maximum* number of flux lines are cut, the voltage is *maximum*. As shown, in a two-pole a-c generator, the voltage passes through zero and maximum *twice* during every full rotation of the loop. This variation follows a *sine wave*. So for one full rotation, which corresponds to 360 degrees of rotation, the generated voltage corresponds to 360 electrical degrees.

By comparing the waveform shown with that on page 6-73, you can see that the output voltage of the simple a-c generator is the same as that induced in the rotating loop of a simple d-c generator.

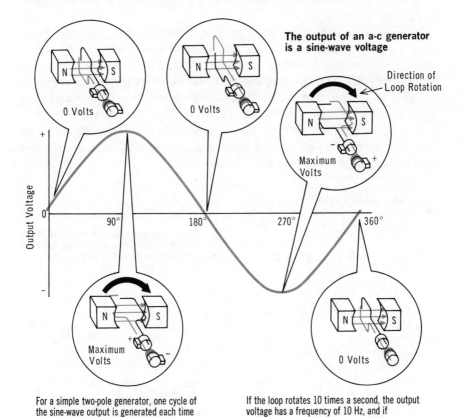

The output of an a-c generator is a sine-wave voltage

0 Volts

0 Volts

Direction of Loop Rotation

Maximum Volts

Output Voltage

90°   180°   270°   360°

Maximum Volts

0 Volts

For a simple two-pole generator, one cycle of the sine-wave output is generated each time the loop makes one full rotation. The frequency of such a generator, therefore, is the same as the speed of rotation of the loop

If the loop rotates 10 times a second, the output voltage has a frequency of 10 Hz, and if the loop rotates 100 times a second, the frequency of the output voltage is 100 Hz

increasing the number of poles

From the waveform on the previous page, you can see that the output voltage of the simple a-c generator is maximum when the sides of the loop pass the centers of the poles. The reason for this is that at these points the sides of the loop are cutting the maximum number of flux lines. If four poles were used instead of two, the output voltage would still reach its maximum value when the sides of the loop passed the centers of the poles. However, since the number of poles was doubled, the voltage would be maximum *four times* during each full rotation of the loop, instead of two times, as it is for a two-pole generator.

If the poles are spaced equally apart, this means that one full sine-wave cycle of the output voltage is generated each time the loop makes one-half, or 180 degrees, of a rotation. The *frequency* of the a-c output voltage is, therefore, *twice* the speed of rotation of the loop. For example, if the loop rotates 30 times a second, the frequency of the voltage is 60 Hz.

It should be obvious that for a given speed of rotation, the more poles there are, the higher will be the frequency of the generator voltage. A general relationship between the speed of rotation of a single loop, the number of poles, and the frequency can be stated as follows: *Frequency is equal to the number of revolutions per second times the number of pairs of poles.* Thus, if six poles are used, the loop rotates 10 times a second, the frequency of the output voltage is 10 × 3, or 30 Hz. Note that it is the number of *pairs* of poles and not the total number of poles that is used in determining the frequency.

In a 4-pole generator, the sides of the loop cut a maximum number of flux lines four times during each full rotation of the loop

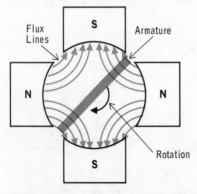

The four points of maximum voltage occur when the sides of the loop pass the centers of the four poles

In a 4-pole generator, two cycles of the output voltage are generated for each full rotation of the loop

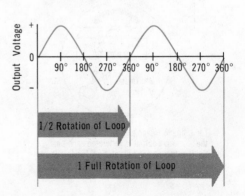

producing the magnetic field

The magnetic field required for the operation of an a-c generator is produced by a *field winding*, the same as it is for d-c generators. You will recall that the field winding is an *electromagnet*, and, therefore, requires current to produce its magnetic field. In a d-c generator, the current for the field winding can be provided by connecting the winding to an external voltage source, in which case the generator is a *separately excited generator*. Or, the exciting current for the field winding can be obtained by connecting the winding to the generator output. This, you will remember, makes it a *self-excited generator*.

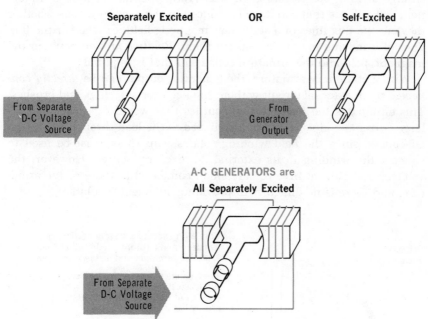

In both cases, though, whether the d-c generator is separately excited or self-excited, the voltage applied to the field winding is dc. This is necessary since a d-c exciting current is required for proper generator operation. As a result, self-excitation *cannot* be used for a-c generators since they have a-c outputs. Separate d-c voltage sources must be used to provide current for the field windings. On many a-c generators, the d-c voltage source for the field winding is a small d-c generator contained in the same housing with the a-c generator.

stationary-armature a-c generators

When an a-c generator delivers a relatively small amount of power, slip rings operate satisfactorily. When large powers are involved, though, it becomes difficult to insulate slip rings sufficiently, and they are therefore a frequent source of trouble. Because of this, most a-c generators have a *stationary armature* and a *rotating field*. In such generators, the armature coils are permanently mounted around the inner circumference of the generator housing, while the field coils and their pole pieces are mounted on a shaft and rotate within the stationary armature. This arrangement of a stationary armature and a rotating field may seem strange at first, but recalling the basic fundamentals of mutual induction, you will see that a voltage is induced in the armature coils whether they cut the flux lines of a stationary magnetic field, or whether the flux lines of a moving magnetic field cut them. *Relative motion* between the magnetic field and the armature coils is all that is required.

With a stationary armature, the generator output can be *directly connected* to an external circuit without the need for slip rings and brushes. This eliminates the insulation difficulties that would otherwise exist if large currents and voltages were delivered to the load through slip rings. Of course, since the field winding rotates, slip rings must be used to connect the winding to its external d-c exciting source. However, the voltages and current involved are small compared to those of the armature, and there is no difficulty in providing sufficient insulation.

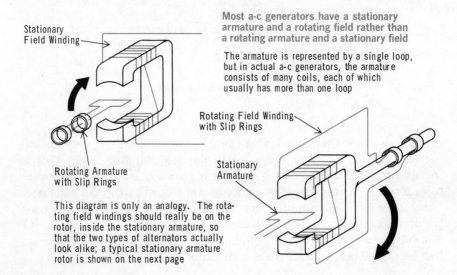

Stationary
Field Winding

Most a-c generators have a stationary armature and a rotating field rather than a rotating armature and a stationary field

The armature is represented by a single loop, but in actual a-c generators, the armature consists of many coils, each of which usually has more than one loop

Rotating Field Winding with Slip Rings

Rotating Armature with Slip Rings

Stationary Armature

This diagram is only an analogy. The rotating field windings should really be on the rotor, inside the stationary armature, so that the two types of alternators actually look alike; a typical stationary armature rotor is shown on the next page

stationary-armature a-c generators (cont.)

Another advantage of using a stationary armature is that it makes possible much higher speeds of rotation, and therefore *higher voltages,* than can be obtained with rotating armatures. The reason for this is again insulating difficulties. At very high speeds of rotation, the large centrifugal force that results makes it difficult to properly insulate the armature winding. No such problem exists when the field winding rotates at high speeds.

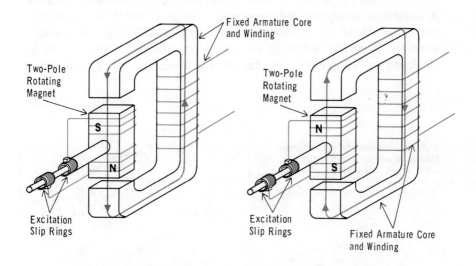

As the field poles in a stationary-armature generator are rotated, the flux lines that go from the N to S poles pass through the fixed-armature core first in one direction and then the other to induce ac in the stationary-armature winding

In summary, then, whereas practically all d-c generators use a rotating armature and a stationary field, most a-c generators have a stationary armature and a rotating field. With a stationary armature, voltages can be produced that are much larger than those possible with rotating-armature generators. The portion of a generator that rotates is often referred to as the *rotor,* while the stationary portion is called the *stator.*

You should note that if a stationary-armature a-c generator uses a *fixed* magnet for the field in the rotor, instead of an electromagnet, no slip rings at all will be required. However, such a generator has a low output, and so is limited in its applications.

single-phase a-c generators

In the discussion of a-c generators, the armature has been represented by a single loop. The voltage induced in such a loop would be very small; so, as in d-c generators, the armature actually consists of a number of coils, each usually having more than one loop. The coils are wound so that the voltages induced in the loops of any one coil *add* to produce the total coil voltage. The coils can be connected in various ways, with the particular method used depending on the desired generator characteristics.

If the armature coils are all connected in series aiding, the generator has a *single output*. The output is sinusoidal, and is equal in amplitude at any instant to the sum of the voltages induced in the individual coils. A generator having its armature wound in this way is a *single-phase generator*. All of the coils connected in series make up the armature winding. Very few practical a-c generators are single phase. Greater efficiency can be gained by connecting the armature coils in other ways.

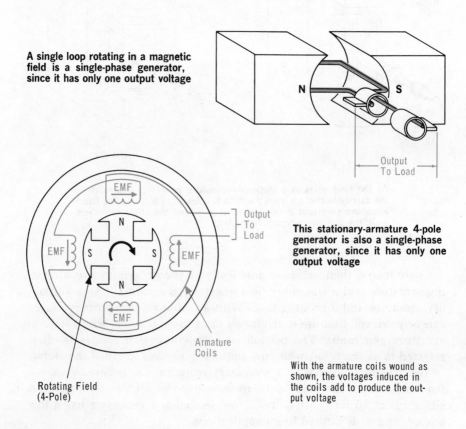

A single loop rotating in a magnetic field is a single-phase generator, since it has only one output voltage

Output To Load

This stationary-armature 4-pole generator is also a single-phase generator, since it has only one output voltage

EMF

Output To Load

EMF   EMF

EMF

Armature Coils

Rotating Field (4-Pole)

With the armature coils wound as shown, the voltages induced in the coils add to produce the output voltage

two-phase a-c generators

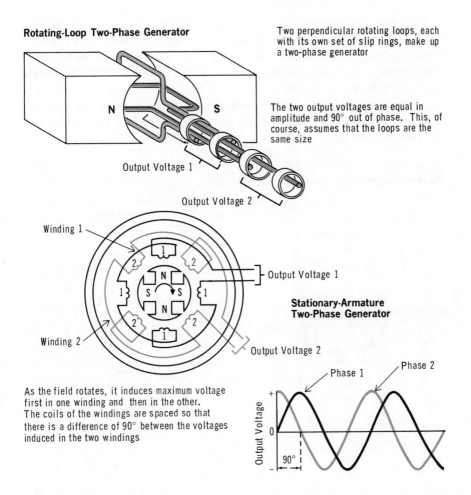

Rotating-Loop Two-Phase Generator

Two perpendicular rotating loops, each with its own set of slip rings, make up a two-phase generator

N   S

The two output voltages are equal in amplitude and 90° out of phase. This, of course, assumes that the loops are the same size

Output Voltage 1

Output Voltage 2

Winding 1

1
2   2
1   S   S   1
N
2   2
1

Output Voltage 1

**Stationary-Armature
Two-Phase Generator**

Winding 2

Output Voltage 2

As the field rotates, it induces maximum voltage first in one winding and then in the other. The coils of the windings are spaced so that there is a difference of 90° between the voltages induced in the two windings

Phase 1   Phase 2

Output Voltage

90°

In a two-phase generator, the armature coils are wired so that the generator has two separate output voltages that differ in phase by 90 degrees. A simple, rotating-loop two-phase generator consists of two loops perpendicular to each other, with each loop connected to its own set of slip rings. When the voltage induced in one loop is maximum, the voltage in the other is zero; and vice versa. The voltages taken from the slip rings, therefore, differ in phase by 90 degrees.

The armature coils of a practical two-phase generator having a stationary armature are divided into two single-phase windings, with the individual coils of the two windings spaced so that the voltages induced in the two windings are 90 degrees out of phase.

three-phase a-c generators

Basically, the principles of a three-phase generator are the same as those of a two-phase generator, except that there are *three equally spaced* windings, and three output voltages all *120 degrees out of phase* with each other. A simple rotating-loop three-phase generator with its output waveforms is shown. Physically adjacent loops are separated by an angle equivalent to 60 degrees of rotation. However, the ends of the loop are connected to the slip rings in such a way that voltage 1 leads voltage 2 by 120 degrees, and voltage 2, in turn, leads voltage 3 by 120 degrees.

Rotating-Loop
Three-Phase Generator

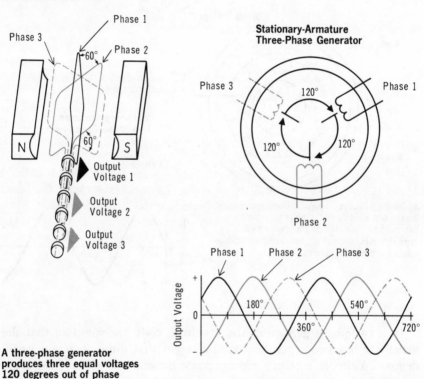

A three-phase generator
produces three equal voltages
120 degrees out of phase

A simplified diagram of a stationary-armature three-phase generator is also shown. On this diagram, the individual coils of each winding are combined, and represented as a single coil. Also, the rotating field is not shown. The significance of the illustration is that it shows that the three-phase generator has three separate armature windings that are 120 degrees out of phase.

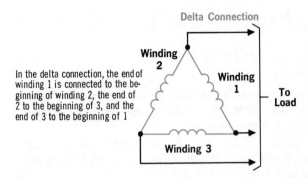

Delta Connection

In the delta connection, the end of winding 1 is connected to the beginning of winding 2, the end of 2 to the beginning of 3, and the end of 3 to the beginning of 1

The three windings thus form a closed circuit. Leads are brought from the three junctions of the windings for connecting to the load. Any 2 of the 3 wires takes the voltage phase across one coil

delta and wye connections

As shown on the previous page, there are six leads from the armature windings of a three-phase generator, and the output voltage is connected to the external load by means of these six leads. In actual practice, this is not the case. Instead, the windings are connected together, and only *three* leads are brought out for connection to the load.

There are two ways that the three armature windings can be connected. Which of the two that is used determines the electrical characteristics of the generator output. In one connection, the three windings are all connected in *series* and form a closed circuit. The load is connected to the three points where two windings are joined. This is called a *delta connection,* since its schematic representation resembles the Greek letter delta (Δ). In the other connection, one of the leads of each winding are connected together, and the other three leads are brought out for connecting the load. This is called a *wye connection,* since schematically it represents the letter Y.

In each case, you can see that the windings are spaced 120 degrees apart, so that each winding will develop a voltage that is 120 degrees out of phase with the other winding voltages.

Wye Connection

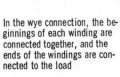

In the wye connection, the beginnings of each winding are connected together, and the ends of the windings are connected to the load

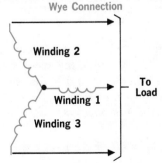

Any two of the 3 wires takes the vector sum of the voltage phases across 2 coils in series

electrical characteristics of delta and wye connections

Since the windings of a delta connection are all connected in series and form a closed circuit, it may seem that a high current will continuously flow through the windings, even when no load is connected. Actually, because of the phase difference between the three generated voltages, negligible or no current flows in the windings under no-load conditions.

The three leads brought out from the delta connection are used for connecting the generator output to the load. The voltage between any two of the leads, called the *line voltage,* is the same as the voltage generated in one winding, which is called the *phase voltage.* Thus, as shown, the three phase voltages are equal and the three line voltages are equal, and they all have the same value. The current in any line, though is $\sqrt{3}$ or approximately 1.73 times the current in any one phase of the winding. You can see, therefore, that a delta connection provides an *increase in current* but *no increase in voltage.*

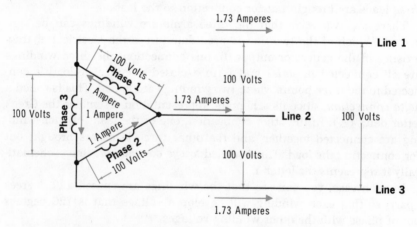

In a delta connection, line voltage equals phase voltage, whereas line current equals √3 or 1.73 times phase current

The total *true power* delivered by a delta-connected three-phase generator is equal to $\sqrt{3}$, or 1.73, times the true power in any one line. Remember, though, from Volumes 3 and 4, that the true power depends on the power factor $(\cos \theta)$ of the circuit. The total true power is therefore equal to 1.73 times the line voltage, times the line current, times the power factor. Or,

$$P_{TRUE} = 1.73 \, E_{LINE} I_{LINE} \cos \theta$$

electrical characteristics of delta and wye connections (cont.)

The voltage and current characteristics of a wye connection are *opposite* to those of a delta connection. The voltage between any two lines of a wye connection is 1.73 times any one phase voltage, while the line currents are equal to the current in any phase winding. This contrasts with the delta connection in which, you will recall, line voltage equals phase voltage and line current equals 1.73 times phase current. Thus, whereas the delta connection provides an increase in current but no increase in voltage, the wye connection gives an increase in voltage but none in current.

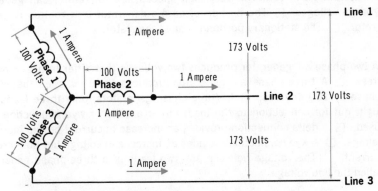

In a wye connection, line voltage equals √3̄ or 1.73 times phase voltage, whereas line current equals phase current

The total *true power* delivered by a wye-connected generator is the same as that of a delta-connected generator. The total true power is therefore equal to:

$$P_{TRUE} = 1.73\, E_{LINE} I_{LINE} \cos \theta$$

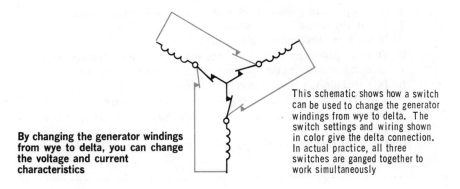

By changing the generator windings from wye to delta, you can change the voltage and current characteristics

This schematic shows how a switch can be used to change the generator windings from wye to delta. The switch settings and wiring shown in color give the delta connection. In actual practice, all three switches are ganged together to work simultaneously

summary

☐ A-c generators are also called alternators. ☐ Since conversion from ac to dc is not required in an a-c generator, a commutator is unnecessary. ☐ The a-c generator uses metallic rings, called slip rings, for connecting the rotating coils to the brushes. ☐ The output frequency of an a-c generator is equal to the frequency of rotation times the number of pairs of poles. ☐ A-c generators cannot be self-excited. Separate d-c voltage sources must be used to provide excitation current.

☐ Most a-c generators have a stationary armature and a rotating field. The generator output is then connected directly to the external circuit. ☐ In a stationary-armature generator, slip rings and brushes are used to connect the rotating field winding to its external d-c exciting source. ☐ Stationary-armature generators can rotate at very high speeds, and therefore, can generate very large voltages. ☐ The portion of an a-c generator that rotates is called the rotor. ☐ The stationary portion is called the stator.

☐ A two-phase a-c generator produces two voltages that differ in phase by 90 degrees. ☐ A three-phase a-c generator produces three voltages that differ in phase by 120 degrees. ☐ In three-phase generators, only three leads are brought out for connection to the load. Either a delta or wye connection can be used. ☐ A delta connection provides an increase in current but no increase in voltage. ☐ A wye connection provides an increase in voltage but no increase in current. ☐ The voltage between any two leads of a three-phase generator is called the line voltage.

review questions

1. Can an a-c generator be self-excited? Why?
2. In an a-c generator, what is the advantage of having a stationary armature and a rotating field?
3. Are slip rings required on a stationary-armature generator?
4. In an alternator, what is the *rotor*? The *stator*?
5. What is a *three-phase a-c generator*?
6. Draw a diagram of a delta connection. A wye connection.
7. In delta and wye connections, what is the line voltage?
8. If a three-phase generator is to supply maximum voltage to a load, would a delta or wye connection be used?
9. What advantages do a-c generators have over d-c generators?
10. Why are commutators unnecessary on a-c generators?

regulating the generator

When the load on an a-c generator changes, the output voltage also tends to change, the same as it does in a d-c generator. The main reason for this is the change in the voltage drop across the armature winding caused by the change in load current. However, whereas in a d-c generator the voltage drop across the armature winding is simply an *IR drop*, in an a-c generator there is an IR drop and an IX_L *drop*, caused by the a-c current flowing through the inductance of the winding. The IR drop depends only on the amount of the load change, but the IX_L drop depends also on the circuit *power factor*. Thus, the output voltage of a-c generators varies with both changes in load current and changes in power factor. As a result, an a-c generator that has satisfactory regulation at one power factor may have very poor regulation at another power factor.

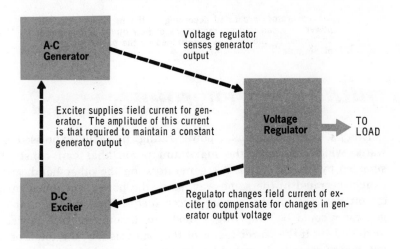

A-C Generator

Voltage regulator senses generator output

Exciter supplies field current for generator. The amplitude of this current is that required to maintain a constant generator output

Voltage Regulator

TO LOAD

D-C Exciter

Regulator changes field current of exciter to compensate for changes in generator output voltage

Because of their inherently poor regulation, a-c generators are generally provided with some auxiliary means of regulation. The auxiliary regulators used, whether they are manually operated or work automatically, accomplish their function in basically the same way. They sense the generator output voltage, and when it changes, they cause a corresponding change in the field current of the exciter that supplies field current to the generator. Thus, if the generator output voltage drops, the regulator causes an increase in the exciter field current. The exciter output voltage, therefore, increases, causing the current in the generator field winding to also increase. As a result, the magnetic field of the generator increases in strength and raises the generator voltage to its original amplitude. A similar, but opposite, sequence of events takes place when the regulator senses a decrease in the generator output voltage.

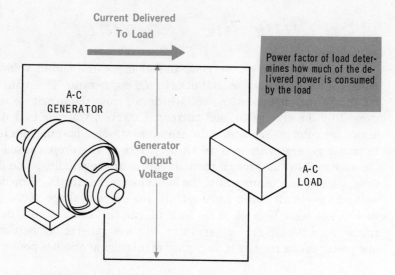

Current Delivered
To Load

A-C
GENERATOR

Generator
Output
Voltage

A-C
LOAD

Power factor of load determines how much of the de-
livered power is consumed
by the load

A-c generators are rated according to the maximum apparent
power they can deliver, regardless of how much of this power is
consumed by the load, as determined by the power factor
of the load

rating a-c generators

Every d-c generator has a power rating, normally expressed in kilowatts, which indicates the maximum power that can constantly be
supplied by the generator. A-c generators, on the other hand, generally
cannot be rated in the same way, since the power *consumed* in an a-c
circuit depends on the circuit *power factor*. This means that an a-c
generator could be supplying a moderate amount of true power for a
load, and yet if the power factor of the load was low, the total, or apparent, power actually delivered by the generator could be very large. Such
a situation could result in the generator burning out.

For this reason, a-c generators must be rated not on the basis of the
maximum allowable power consumption of the load, but on the basis of
the *maximum apparent power* they can deliver. This is done by express-
ing the capacity in *volt-amperes,* or *kilovolt-amperes.* Thus, at any particular output voltage, you know the maximum current that the generator can deliver, regardless of the power factor of the load. For example,
if an a-c generator with a rating of 100 kilovolt-amperes has an output
of 50 kilovolts, the maximum current that it can safely deliver is 100
kilovolt-amperes divided by 50 kilovolts, or 2 amperes.

Occasionally, a-c generators are designed for use with loads having a
constant power factor. The rating of these generators then may be given
in watts or kilowatts *at the particular power factor.*

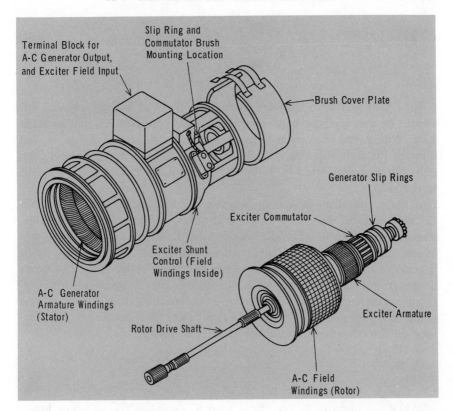

construction of a-c generators

From the standpoint of physical appearance, a-c generators vary considerably. They range from very large turbine-driven types that weigh thousands of pounds to small special-purpose types that weigh only a few pounds, and even less. As has been pointed out, though, practically all a-c generators have stationary armatures and rotating fields. The armature windings are positioned around the inner circumference of the generator housing, and are usually embedded in a laminated iron core. The core and the windings make up the stator.

The field winding and field poles, which make up the rotor, are mounted on a shaft, and turn within the stator. Also mounted on the rotor shaft are the slip rings for the field windings. When the generator contains its own d-c exciter, the exciter armature and commutator are also mounted on the motor shaft. The brush holders for the generator slip rings and the exciter commutator are mounted on the generator housing, as are terminals for making electrical connections to the generator. A typical a-c generator with a self-contained exciter is shown.

comparison of d-c and a-c generators

Now that you have learned about both d-c and a-c generators, you should be aware of the basic *similarities* between them as well as their basic *differences*. In an a-c generator, the induced voltage is fed directly through slip rings to the load, while in a d-c generator, the induced ac is converted to dc by the commutator before being applied to the load.

A major physical difference between d-c and a-c generators is that the field of most d-c generators is stationary and the armature rotates, whereas the opposite is usually true of a-c generators. This has the effect of making a-c generators capable of having much larger outputs than is possible with d-c generators. Another difference between the two types of generators is the source of exciting voltage for the field winding. D-c generators can either use a separate external exciting source, or can obtain the required voltage directly from their own output. A-c generators, on the other hand, must use a separate source.

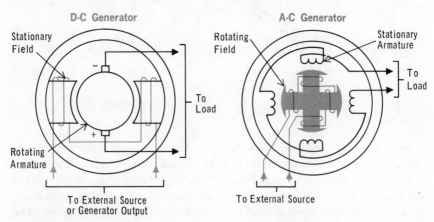

The d-c generator has a rotating armature and a stationary field. Voltage for its field can be obtained either from an external source or from the generator's own output

The a-c generator has a stationary armature and a rotating field. Voltage for its field must come from an external source, called an exciter

In the area of voltage regulation, d-c generators are inherently more stable than a-c generators. One of the reasons for this is that although the output voltages of both types are sensitive to load changes, the output voltage of an a-c generator is also sensitive to changes in the power factor of the load. In addition, a good degree of self-regulation is possible in a d-c generator by using a compound armature winding. This is not possible in a-c generators, since they must be separately excited.

the automobile alternator

The comparison of the advantages of d-c generators and a-c alternators, which you just studied, was based on the accepted categories of basic generators. However, it is possible to combine the advantages of d-c and a-c generators by using additional circuit designs. The automobile alternator does this in a unique way to produce a high-current d-c charging source with an a-c type of generator. It is called an alternator even though it produces a d-c voltage because it is actually a fixed-armature a-c generator that uses *rectifiers* to convert the ac to dc.

Rectifiers are devices that, for the most part, conduct in only one direction. So, the rectifier will pass only one polarity of the a-c voltage to produce a pulsating dc. The typical car alternator produces three-phase ac, so that after the voltage is converted to dc, there is less ripple. A capacitor is then connected at the output to filter out the ripple to get a relatively smooth d-c voltage.

Because the rectifiers oppose current flow in the opposite direction, a reverse-current cutout relay is not needed in the voltage regulator. And, since the alternator is a high-current generator, a current regulator also is not needed. Therefore, the regulator for the alternator is simpler than that for the d-c generator; it uses only one relay circuit to regulate the alternator output voltage by controlling the field current. Notice that although this is an alternator, it *is* self-excited. The more recent alternator circuits use electronic regulators instead of relays. These are actually *semiconductor* devices similar to transistors which can be turned on and off just like a relay. They are sometimes called *solid-state relays* because they control the on-off current flow in the same way. This can be done because the rectified output is *dc*.

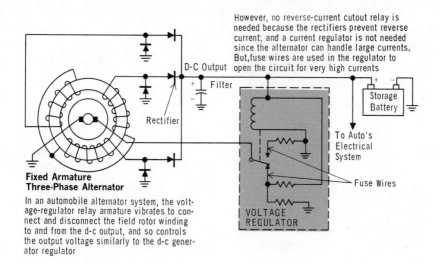

However, no reverse-current cutout relay is needed because the rectifiers prevent reverse current; and a current regulator is not needed since the alternator can handle large currents. But, fuse wires are used in the regulator to open the circuit for very high currents

D-C Output

Filter

Rectifier

Storage Battery

To Auto's Electrical System

Fuse Wires

Fixed Armature Three-Phase Alternator

VOLTAGE REGULATOR

In an automobile alternator system, the voltage-regulator relay armature vibrates to connect and disconnect the field rotor winding to and from the d-c output, and so controls the output voltage similarly to the d-c generator regulator

auto alternator operation

The three-phase auto alternator uses wye-connected fixed-armature windings, which as you learned, produce one phase voltage between any two output leads. The output of the alternator is a positive voltage with relation to ground. But *no* lead of the wye windings is connected directly to ground because the windings produce ac; all three leads alternately become negative and positive through the a-c cycles. Therefore, each lead must be connected to ground when it is negative, and to the output when it is positive. The rectifiers do this.

The rectifiers act like switches that close for one polarity, and open for the other polarity. Notice that each lead has two rectifiers connected oppositely. One rectifier will connect the lead to the output line when the lead is positive, but disconnect the lead when it is negative. The other rectifier connects the lead to ground when it is negative, and disconnects it when it is positive. The diagram shows how the same two windings are connected for different phase angles of the output voltage. The output, then, is always positive.

If you recall what you learned about the d-c generator, you can see that the commutator was needed to do the same thing whenever the leads switched polarity, since the armature always produces ac. In the alternator, then, the rectifiers act like electronic commutators, and so it is debatable about whether the alternator *is* an alternator, or just another type of d-c generator.

Three-Phase Commutation

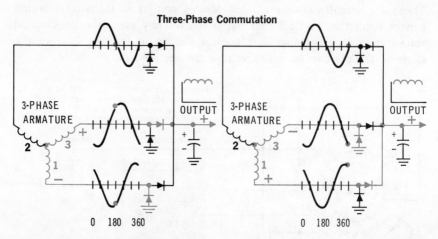

Only two possibilities are shown here. At 120 degrees, winding 2 would be positive and so would be connected to the output instead of winding 3, which would be set at zero volts. Winding 1 would still be negative.

At 60 degrees, winding 3 would be negative and go to ground, while winding 2 would be positive and go to the output. At the intermediate phase angles, it is possible to have two windings connected to the output and one to ground, and vice versa

internal resistance of the generator

In every generator, the load current flows through the armature winding. Like any coil or winding, the armature has *resistance* and *inductance*. The combination of this resistance and the inductive reactance caused by the inductance make up what is known as the *internal resistance* of the generator. When load current flows, it produces a voltage drop across the internal resistance. This voltage drop subtracts from the generator output voltage, and, therefore, represents generated voltage that is *lost* and not available for the load.

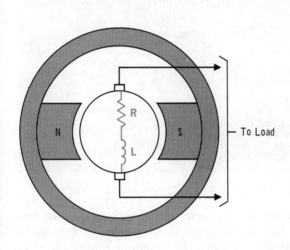

The armature winding of every generator has resistance and inductance. The resistance and the reactance caused by the inductance make up the internal resistance of the generator

Whenever load current flows, it is opposed by the internal resistance. This opposition produces a voltage drop that subtracts from the generator output voltage

You can see that the larger the internal resistance is, the greater is the portion of the generated voltage that is dropped within the generator and thus lost. In a d-c generator with a given internal resistance, the internal voltage drop is directly proportional to the load current, and is equal to:

$$E = I_{LOAD}R_{INTERNAL}$$

Thus, the greater the load current, the more voltage is dropped across the internal resistance. In an a-c generator, the internal voltage drop also depends on the *frequency* of the generator output voltage, since the inductive reactance of the armature winding changes whenever the frequency does. Inasmuch as the generator speed is one of the factors that determines the frequency, the internal resistance of an a-c generator will change with generator speed.

the motor-generator

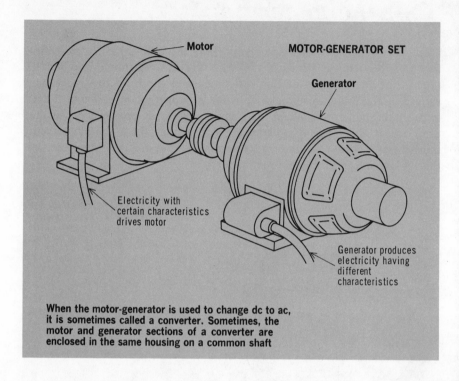

MOTOR-GENERATOR SET

Motor

Generator

Electricity with certain characteristics drives motor

Generator produces electricity having different characteristics

When the motor-generator is used to change dc to ac, it is sometimes called a converter. Sometimes, the motor and generator sections of a converter are enclosed in the same housing on a common shaft

A motor-generator consists of an electric motor and a generator mechanically connected so that the motor turns the generator. The *motor* thus supplies the *mechanical energy* that the *generator* converts to *electrical energy*. Normally, both the motor and the generator of a motor-generator are mounted on the same baseplate, and are moved about and installed as a single unit.

Motor-generators are usually used to *change* electricity from one voltage or frequency to another voltage or frequency, or to convert ac to dc or dc to ac. Electricity having the characteristic to be changed powers the motor, and the generator is designed to produce electricity having the new desired characteristic. For example, the motor could be driven by a 60-Hz power source, while the generator produces an output having a frequency of 400 Hz. Or, a d-c motor could drive an a-c generator to accomplish dc to ac conversion.

When the device changes ac of one type to ac of another type, or ac to dc, it is referred to as a *motor-generator set*. But, when it is used to convert dc to ac, it is sometimes called a *converter*. Quite often, the converter has the motor and the generator in the same housing.

the dynamotor

In certain respects, the dynamotor is actually a motor-generator. It consists of an electric motor driving a generator. However, a motor-generator set usually uses separate units; in a dynamotor, they are always contained in a *common housing,* similar to the converter, and their armature windings are both wound on the *same shaft.*

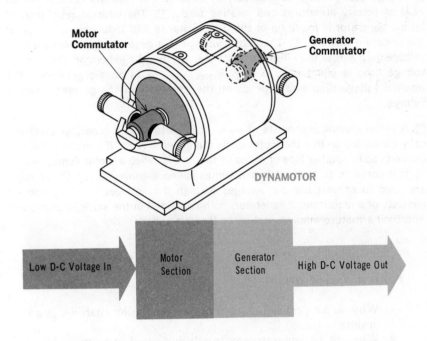

A dynamotor converts a low d-c voltage to a high d-c voltage. Both the motor and the generator portions are mounted on a common shaft and in a common housing

Dynamotors are used for converting *low d-c voltages,* usually supplied by batteries, to *high d-c voltages.* The low voltage drives the motor, turning the generator, which then produces a higher voltage. Dynamotors are frequently used with communications equipment to supply d-c voltages higher than those available from batteries. They are quite common in aircraft, where many kinds of electronic equipment need a few hundred volts of dc to operate, and the main line of the aircraft only supplies 28 volts dc. Some amateur radio equipment, which must operate from the 6- or 12-volt batteries in cars also rely on dynamotors to change the voltage to the required d-c level.

summary

☐ The output voltage of an a-c generator varies with changes in load current and with circuit power factor. ☐ Regulators for a-c generators control the exciter current to the field winding to compensate for changes in output voltage. ☐ A-c generators are rated on the basis of the maximum apparent power they can deliver.

☐ A-c generators vary considerably in appearance. However, practically all have stationary armatures and rotating fields. ☐ The internal resistance of an a-c generator is made up of the d-c resistance and inductive reactance of the armature winding. ☐ The output voltage of a generator is reduced by the voltage drop across the internal resistance. ☐ In a d-c generator, the internal voltage drop is equal to: $E = I_{LOAD} R_{INTERNAL}$. ☐ In an a-c generator, the internal voltage drop also depends on the frequency of the generator output voltage.

☐ A motor-generator consists of an electric motor and a generator mechanically connected so that the motor turns the generator. ☐ If a motor-generator converts ac to another type of ac, or ac to dc, it is called a motor-generator set. ☐ If it converts dc to ac, it is sometimes called a converter. ☐ Dynamotors are used to convert low d-c voltages to high d-c voltages. ☐ A dynamotor consists of a motor and a generator, both contained in the same housing, and with their armature windings wound on the same shaft.

review questions

1. Why do a-c generators have poorer regulation than d-c generators?
2. Why are a-c generators normally not rated in watts or kilowatts?
3. An a-c generator has a rating of 20 kilovolt-amperes and an output of 2 kilovolts. What is the maximum current it can safely deliver?
4. What things affect the internal resistance of an a-c generator?
5. What are motor-generators used for?
6. What is a *converter*?
7. What is a dynamotor used for?
8. If the power factor of the load decreases while the generator output voltage and current remain constant, what happens to the true power delivered by an a-c generator?
9. If the speed of an a-c generator is increased, what happens to the internal resistance?
10. Does generator speed affect the internal resistance of a d-c generator?

index